The Cell

The Cell

CARL P. SWANSON

William D. Gill Professor in Biology
The Johns Hopkins University

Prentice-Hall, Inc.

ENGLEWOOD CLIFFS, NEW JERSEY

The Cell

Carl P. Swanson

© *Copyright* 1960
by PRENTICE-HALL, INC.,
Englewood Cliffs, New Jersey.

PRENTICE-HALL FOUNDATIONS OF MODERN BIOLOGY SERIES

William D. McElroy and Carl P. Swanson, *Editors*

Eighth printing......June, 1963

Design by Walter Behnke

Drawings by Felix Cooper

12157-C

To **D.N.S.** *for many reasons*

The science of biology today is *not* the same science of fifty, twenty-five, or even ten years ago. Today's accelerated pace of research, aided by new instruments, techniques, and points of view, imparts to biology a rapidly changing character as discoveries pile one on top of the other. All of us are aware, however, that each new and important discovery is not just a mere addition to our knowledge; it also throws our established beliefs into question, and forces us constantly to reappraise and often to reshape the foundations upon which biology rests. An adequate presentation of the dynamic state of modern biology is, therefore, a formidable task and a challenge worthy of our best teachers.

The authors of this series believe that a new approach to the organization of the subject matter of biology is urgently needed to meet this challenge, an approach that introduces the student to biology as a growing, active science, and that also *permits each teacher of biology to determine the level and the structure of his own course.* A single textbook cannot provide such flexibility, and it is the authors' strong conviction that these student needs and teacher prerogatives can best be met by a series of short, inexpensive, well-written, and well-illustrated books so planned as to encompass those areas of study central to an understanding of the content, state, and direction of modern biology. The FOUNDATIONS OF MODERN BIOLOGY SERIES represents the translation of these ideas into print, with each volume being complete in itself yet at the same time serving as an integral part of the series as a whole.

ix

Contents

The struggle to know is one of the most exciting dramas of history, and every man who ever tried to learn anything has enacted it for himself to some extent.
—RICHARD R. POWELL

1

Introduction

The universe around us is not a continuum, a sort of pea-soupy structureless fog. Common experience tells us that it is made up of objects, matter, and other associated phenomena that we can describe or measure. We soon realize that each of these "things" has a uniqueness that we detect through touch, taste, hearing, smell, or sight, and that each is distinguishable to a greater or lesser degree. With our unaided senses, we have no difficulty in distinguishing the sky and the land from the water, a gas and a solid from a liquid, the living from the nonliving. On a more refined level, we can discriminate degrees of roughness, intensity and shade of color (provided we are not colorblind), and an acid taste from one that is salty, sweet, or bitter. But human powers of sensory discrimination are limited. We hear only within a certain range of sound waves, and see only a certain portion of the light spectrum (Fig. 1). When we try to go beyond these limits, we can no longer directly comprehend the physical nature of things and must resort to instruments to penetrate areas outside our naturally circumscribed sphere.

Instruments, therefore, act as extended senses. The 200-inch Hale telescope on Mount Palomar reaches across millions of light-years to bring distant galaxies of the macrocosm into view, while light microscopes and electron microscopes reach down into the microcosm to reveal otherwise invisible worlds. Similarly, the photographic plate, more

1

sensitive than our eyes, extends our use of light rays. Ordinarily we can see only a minute portion of the electromagnetic spectrum, but by utilizing photosensitive surfaces we can detect the long infrared rays on one side of the spectrum and the short ultraviolet rays, X-rays, and even cosmic rays on the other.

By whatever means we use, the "things" we observe are called *units*, and the more refined is our knowledge and the more powerful and discriminating our instruments and techniques, the more precise becomes our definition of these units, i.e., their limits and their basic nature and function. If we are interested in classification, we find that these units often group themselves into meaningful systems. It would, indeed, be impossible for you to read these pages without understanding letters, the basic units of our language, or the numbers that make up our decimal system. The periodic table of atoms is another example of such a coherent system, and part of its great value lies in the fact that it enables us to predict what will happen under specified physical or chemical circumstances. The study of a related group of these systems quite often develops into a separate science. One of the first goals of a science, therefore, whether it be physics, chemistry, or biology, is to determine the uniqueness of the units with which it is concerned, for unless such units are understood and accepted by everyone in a particular field, scientific knowledge in it cannot progress.

Fig. I. The electromagnetic spectrum on a linear log scale, measured in millimeters (mm), microns (μ), and Angstrom units (Å). Their relation to each other is as follows: 1 μ = 0.001 mm = 10,000 Å. At top are given the approximate lower limits of resolution of the human eye, the light microscope, and the electron microscope.

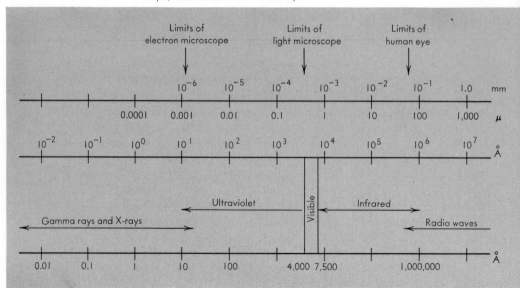

It should be pointed out that science makes use of two kinds of units. Those used to describe time, weight, and distance are arbitrarily defined, but we accept them as standards for the sake of convenience. Those such as the electron, proton, and neutron, however, have a demonstrated physical reality which can be independently determined by anyone having the proper instruments and required knowledge.

It is the latter type of unit that we will investigate here, for the basic unit of life, the *cell*, is a physical entity. We can break cells up and extract selected parts of them for study much as the physicist breaks up atoms. We find that these cellular fragments can carry on many of their activities for a time; they may consume oxygen, ferment sugars, and even form new molecules. But these activities individually do not constitute life any more than the behavior of a subatomic particle is equivalent to the behavior of an intact atom. The disrupted cell is no longer capable of continuing life indefinitely, so we conclude that the cell is the most elemental unit that can sustain life.

Compared to the atom and the molecule, the cell, of course, is a unit of far greater size and complexity. It is a microcosm having a definite boundary, within which a constant chemical activity is going on. The only chemically quiescent cell is a dead one. The function of *cytology* (the science of cells), therefore, is to recognize the kinds of cells that exist, to understand their organization and structure in terms of their activities and functions, and to visualize the cell not only as an individual microcosm (as it is, for example, in the unicellular bacterium) but also as an integral part of the more elaborate organs and organ systems of multicellular plants and animals.

Historical Background

The now familiar idea that the cell is the basic unit of life is known as the *cell theory* or the *cell doctrine*. Enunciated in 1839 by two German scientists, M. J. Schleiden and Theodor Schwann, the former a botanist and the latter a zoologist, the cell doctrine represented a decisive advance in the development of biological thought which now ranks with Charles Darwin's *evolution theory* as one of the foundation stones of modern biology. Indeed, we understand life itself only to the extent that we understand the structure and function of cells. As one scientist [1] has so aptly stated: "the cell concept is the concept of life, its origin, its nature and its continuity."

---

[1] J. S. Karling, "Schleiden's Contribution to the Cell Theory," *Biological Symposia,* I (1940).

The emergence of a great scientific generalization is generally a slow accumulative process; very few men and their ideas stand alone in the stream of time. The significance of the date 1839 and of the names Schleiden and Schwann, therefore, does not lie in the fact that these men discovered cells, for the existence of cells had been known since 1665 when the Englishman, Robert Hooke, first saw them in a piece of cork under his primitive microscope (Fig. 2). It was Hooke, incidentally, who coined the word *cell* to designate the tiny structures he observed in the new world he had discovered. Nor indeed were Schleiden and Schwann the first to believe in, or advance, the idea that plants and animals were composed of cells and cell products; the Frenchman, Dutrochet, had stated this clearly some fifteen years earlier. The authors of the cell theory were, in fact, quite incorrect in some of their conclusions about the origin of cells. What they did do, however, was take the loose threads of old ideas and observations and weave them into a meaningful whole. Theirs

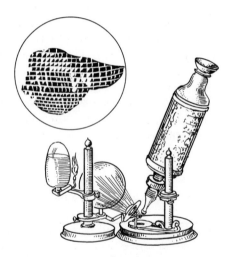

Fig. 2. Robert Hooke's drawing of the microscopic structure of cork (in circle), and the microscope with which he observed it. Here, in his own words, is a description of his experiment: "I took a good clear piece of Cork and with a Pen-knife sharpen'd as keen as a razor, I cut a piece of it off, and thereby left the surface of it exceeding smooth, then examining it very diligently with a Microscope, me thought I could perceive it to appear a little porous; but I could not so plainly distinguish them as to be sure that they were pores. . . . I with the same sharp pen-knife cut off from the former smooth surface an exceeding thin piece of it, and placing it on a black object Plate. . . . and casting the light on it with a deep plano-convex Glass, I could exceedingly plainly perceive it to be all perforated and porous, much like a Honeycomb, but that the pores of it were not regular . . . these pores, or cells, were not very deep, but consisted of a great many little Boxes, separated out of one continued long pore by certain Diaphragms . . . Nor is this kind of texture peculiar to Cork onely; for upon examination with my Microscope, I have found that the pith of an Elder, or almost any other Tree, the inner pulp or pith of the Cany hollow stalks of several other Vegetables: as of Fennel, Carrets, Daucus, Bur-docks, Teasels, Fearn . . . & c. have much such a kind of Schematisme, as I have lately shewn that of Cork."

was an act of synthesis and emphasis rather than of discovery, and by visualizing the cell as both the structural and functional unit of organization, *they defined the basic unit of life.*

Biology lagged behind the physical sciences in its definition of fundamental units. The Greeks as early as the fourth and fifth centuries B.C. speculated that all matter was composed of indivisible "atoms." Their concept, however, was more a philosophical idea than a scientific theory, since they failed to put it to a test or to inspire anyone else in the centuries following to do so. It remained for the Englishman, John Dalton, to accomplish in the early nineteenth century what the Greeks did not; his theory ascribed to the atom specific properties that not only explained many physical and chemical phenomena in a reasonable way but also indicated the directions in which systematic investigations of matter could proceed. In other words, *his theory defined the physical basis of matter and gave it predictable properties.* That Dalton's theory, like the cell theory, was not entirely correct is of small concern; what is important is that the two theories, by designating the fundamental unit of matter on the one hand and of life on the other, focused attention on the structures that had to be understood if the respective sciences were to progress.

Some twenty years after the announcements of Schleiden and Schwann, Rudolf Virchow, the great German physician, made another important generalization: that cells come only from pre-existing cells. When biologists further recognized that sperm and eggs are also cells which unite with each other in the process of fertilization, it became clear that life is an uninterrupted succession of cells. Growth, development, inheritance, evolution, disease, aging, and death are, therefore, but varied aspects of cellular behavior. It is with these problems, then, that we will be concerned in this book.

Exceptions to the Cell Theory

Most generalizations have exceptions to them which cast doubt on their universal validity. This is true as well for the cell theory, and the viruses in particular present a difficult problem.

Over three hundred different viruses are known. Many of them are the infective agents in such diseases as yellow fever, rabies, poliomyelitis, small pox, mumps, and measles in humans, and peach yellows and tobacco mosaic disease in plants. The plant viruses tend to be elongated structures, the animal ones spherical in shape (Fig. 3). If we apply to them our usual definition of a cell, they do not qualify as living organisms. Since they are so minute, we cannot see them except through an electron microscope, but we know that they lack the internal organization normally

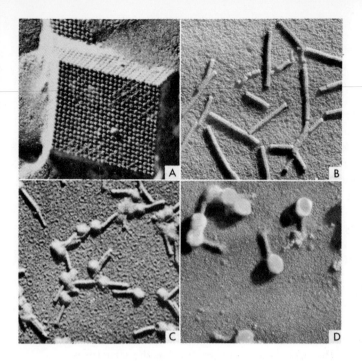

Fig. 3. Electron micrographs of viruses. (A) Tobacco necrosis virus; the virus particles are spherical in shape and about 250 Å in diameter, but when precipitated in ammonium sulfate they form a crystalline structure. (B) Tobacco mosaic virus; each rod is made up of a stack of plates similar to a stack of coins, with a protein coat on the outside and an inner core of ribose nucleic acid. (C) P2 bacteriophage or bacterial virus, which attacks the colon bacterium; each is equipped with a somewhat hexagonal head and a tail. (D) T6 bacteriophage, which also attacks the colon bacterium. (Courtesy of Dr. L. W. Labaw.)

Fig. 4. Organisms that should be considered acellular rather than cellular, since they lack cross walls. (A) *Paramecium*, the slipper animalcule, which has a mouth, a gullet for ingestion of food, food vacuoles for digestion, contractile vacuoles for excretion, and cilia for movement; (B) *Rhizopus*, the bread mold, with root-like structures to penetrate the surface, aerial branches to raise it into the air, and asexual reproductive structures at the ends of branches; (C) Young plant of *Vaucheria*, the alga which forms green mats on damp soil; (D) Reproduction in *Vaucheria* by the rounding off of a tip of a branch to form an asexual spore which will germinate to produce a new plant.

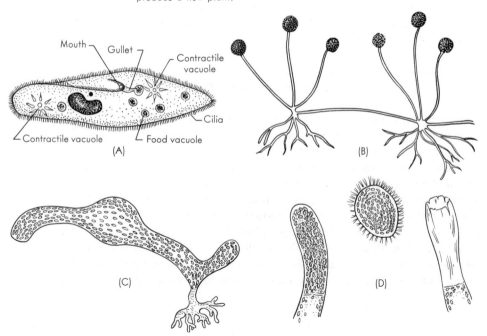

considered indispensable to a functioning cell. When they exist outside a living cell, they are simply inert molecules, although very elaborate and complex ones that may take a crystalline form. Inside a cell, however, where they are pathological parasites, they are clothed with the characteristics of life: they grow, multiply to produce exact replicas of themselves, and possess a type of inheritance not too far different from our own. They also contain the key molecules of protein and nucleic acid invariably found in every living organism.

Their ambiguous nature has led biologists to describe them in various ways: living chemicals; cellular forms that have degenerated through parasitism; or primitive organisms that have not reached a cellular state. Fortunately, we are not forced to decide whether a virus is or is not a cell, or even whether it is living or nonliving. The biologist generally treats them as if they were individual cells, and recognizes that their extreme simplicity of structure, when compared to a normal cell, makes them ideal objects for certain types of biological research.

Certain protozoa, algae, and fungi also provide exceptions to the concept that the cell is the basic unit of life. They appear to have abandoned the cell as a mechanical and structural unit, although their ancestral forms probably once had cells. The protozoan, *Paramecium* (Fig. 4), is seemingly a single cell, but it has a mouth or *gullet, contractile vacuoles* for the elimination of water and waste, other vacuoles for digestion, and many *cilia* (fine surface hairs) for motility. Although the point is debatable, *Paramecium* is probably best thought of as noncellular rather than cellular in nature.

A similar designation can be given to certain algae such as *Valonia,* or *Vaucheria,* or to fungi such as the black bread mold, *Rhizopus* (Fig. 4). They are simply a mass of living substance within an outer retaining wall, and it would be difficult to define the basic unit of such living bodies. These organisms, however, are related to cellular forms, so we can speculate that they have simply discarded the usual type of cellular organization for one that is mechanically better suited to their mode of existence.

Tools and Techniques of Cytology

Progress in the life sciences has not followed an even course, for it has been dependent on the development of more and more refined tools and techniques of analysis. This has been especially true for cytology. Some cells may be large enough to see with the unaided eye. But to identify their internal organization we must magnify them greatly and, more often than not, use dyes that stain selected parts of the cell and not others.

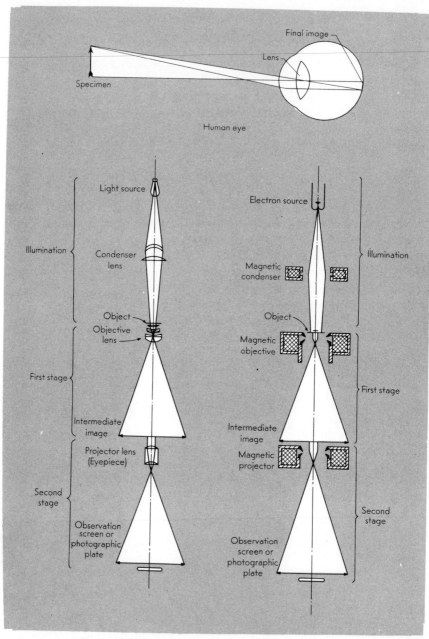

Fig. 5. Schematic representation of the optical systems of the light microscope, and the electron microscope.

Adequate magnification is as much of a problem for the cytologist as it is for the astronomer; the latter has to overcome great distances, the former very small sizes, in their attempts to study in greater detail the objects they observe. For our purposes, the problem of magnification can best be considered in terms of *resolving power,* which is the property of an optical system to distinguish objects lying very close together. In observing a double star, for example, some individuals will be able to discern but a single star; others, with better resolving power, will see two separate stars. In a microscope, the resolving power of the magnifying lens is the critical factor. As Fig. 5 indicates, the lens nearest the specimen being examined, i.e., the *objective,* is the key element of the compound microscope, because the uppermost lens, the *ocular,* can enlarge only what the objective has resolved.

The unaided human eye has a resolving power of 0.025 to 0.1 millimeter. Lines closer together than this will be seen as a single line, while objects that have a diameter smaller than this range will be invisible or seen only as blurred images. The human eye, however, has no power of magnification; each of us must calculate sizes mentally, and experience is probably the largest factor in our ability to judge accurately. Microscopes, of course, both resolve and magnify, but their resolving power is limited by the kind of illumination used. Objects that are less than one-half the wavelength of light apart cannot be distinguished in a light microscope. Thus, even with the most perfectly ground lenses, with white light having an average wavelength of 5,500 Angstroms (Å),[1] the objective cannot resolve objects with a diameter less than 2,750 Å, or 0.275 microns (μ). Since many parts of the cell have lesser dimensions, their presence remained undetected until a means of greater resolution was found.

The *electron microscope* provides this increased resolving power by making use of an "illumination" of a different sort. High-speed *electrons* are employed instead of light. As these pass through the specimen being viewed, the more dense parts of the cell deflect or absorb more electrons than less dense regions, forming an image of the specimen on an electron-sensitive photographic plate or fluorescent screen. The human eye, of course, is not stimulated by electrons, hence the need for plates or screens. The "optical" system is similar to that in the light microscope (Fig. 5) except that the "illumination" is focused by electromagnetic lenses instead of conventional glass lenses.

When electrons are propelled through the microscope by a charge of 50,000 volts, they have a wavelength of about 0.05 Å. This is 1/100,000 that of average white light. An electron microscope can thus theoretically resolve objects with a diameter of one-half of 0.05 Å, or 0.025 Å. This dimension is far less than the diameter of an atom (the hydrogen atom has a diameter of 1.06 Å), but due to difficulties in lens construction, the actual resolving power of the best modern instrument is about 10 Å. In

---

[1] 10,000 Å = 1.0 micron = 0.001 mm.

approximate figures, then, the human eye can resolve down to 100 μ, the light microscope to 0.2 μ, and the electron microscope to 0.001 μ. Or, to put it another way, if the human eye has a resolving power of 1, that of the light microscope is 500, and that of the electron microscope 10,000. The electron microscope has thus opened up a whole new domain to the cytologist, making a number of cellular structures visible for the first time.

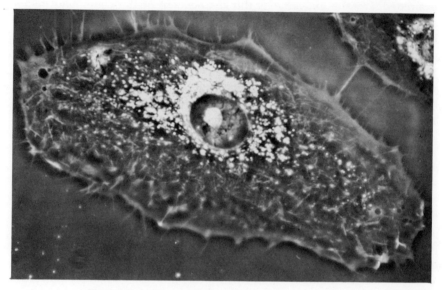

Fig. 6. A human cancer cell (HeLa strain) grown in tissue culture and photographed through a phase-contrast microscope. The nucleus is seen in the center; the white mass is liquid material taken in from the culture medium; the slender rods inside the cell are mitochondria; and the outer fine projections are microfibrils formed by free cells when cultured in test tubes. (Courtesy of Dr. George O. Gey.)

In the study of cells, more than just clear resolution and high magnification are required; the parts of the cell must be clearly distinguished from their immediate surroundings. In the electron microscope, this contrast is possible because some structures are more electron "dense" than others, and the photosensitive film is darkened to the degree that it is struck by the electrons that pass through the specimen. Such contrast is difficult to achieve with the light microscope because direct light passes through most parts of the cell with equal ease. To overcome this problem, the cytologist uses the proper killing agent (fixative) and stain to bring out the parts he wishes to examine (Fig. 6). Literally hundreds of fixing and staining procedures are known; they are the cytologist's "recipes," and he continually improves upon them in his search for better ways to study cells. The very active fields of *cytochemistry* and *histochemistry*, which deal respectively with the chemistry of cells and tissues, are greatly dependent upon these procedures.

A living cell, however, is always more fascinating than a dead one. To watch cells divide is to witness one of the most dramatic of biological phenomena. The *phase-contrast microscope* permits the cytologist to do this. A complicated instrument, with optical properties not yet clearly understood, it gets its name from the fact that various parts of the living cell stand out in sharp contrast when oblique light is passed through. Figure 6 is a photograph of a living human cancer cell, taken through a phase-contrast microscope. Under the conventional light microscope, such a cell would appear almost structureless.

Another way to study living cells is, literally, to "grind" them up and examine their parts. This is done with a special mortar and pestle so as to burst the cells and release their contents into a solution. This solution is then centrifuged at carefully regulated speeds; the heavier portions sediment out at lower speeds, the lighter ones at higher speeds. Even the most elusive cellular components can be obtained in substantial amounts and relatively free of other parts. Once separated, each portion can be analyzed for chemical content or tested for activity, since in the test tube some parts continue to function for a while as they did in the intact cell.

The cytologist, therefore, has a large and varied arsenal of instruments for making the cell give up its secrets. Any one tool or technique, however, is not enough, and several methods are usually employed before an answer can be found to the particular problem being investigated. Such knowledge as we have already garnered from the cell has only strengthened our belief that it is the basis of life, while at the same time making us acutely aware of how little we know of its many complexities.

**2 Cells
in General**

List, if you will, the organs of your body. Even if your knowledge of biology comes only from a casual reading of the daily newspaper or an occasional magazine, the list would be a substantial one: muscles, nerves, skin, eyes, and bones, to mention a few of the more obvious ones. Supplement this list with others from the animal kingdom: the richly colored feathers of the pheasant, hair from the beautifully patterned zebra, the horny outer wing of a beetle, the gossamer wing of a lunar moth. Add, for good measure, examples from the plant world: the thorn of a rose, a wind-blown seed of the milkweed, the soft wood of balsa and the tough wood of oak, the needle-like leaf of the pine.

Obviously this is a miscellany of organs, having very little in common as far as outward appearances and functions are concerned. Yet they share one single feature: they are made up of cells (which are, or have been, bounded on their outer perimeters by a *membrane*), each of which possesses a *nucleus* that acts as the central controlling mechanism and a semi-viscous *cytoplasm* that occupies the remainder of the cellular interior. Each of these cellular parts, as well as other less obvious ones, will be examined in detail in the next chapter; when we examine these varied organs microscopically, we find their constituent cells to be of many different kinds. In fact, there are many more kinds than there are organs, since many organs consist of more than a single cell type. Only a few such glimpses are needed to impress upon us the fact that the cell is a wonderfully plastic unit, capable of varying greatly to meet the many demands of the organism. No sculptor or construction engineer has so versatile a medium with which to work.

Cell Shape

Let us first take a look at those organisms that are unicellular. The entire organism consists of but a single cell. When we remember that *protoplasm* (the name applied to all the living contents of a cell) is a viscous substance bounded by a semi-elastic outer membrane, we naturally assume that the shape of these cells would be spherical, since their surface tension, particularily in those that are free-floating, should form them in the same way that surface tension shapes air-borne soap bubbles and

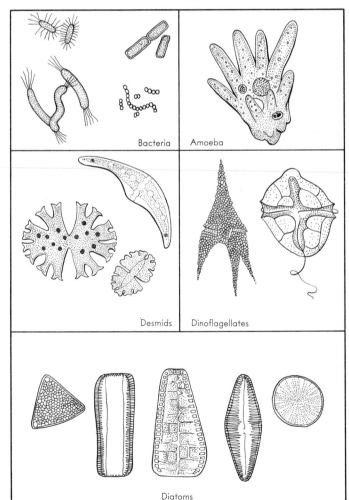

Fig. 7. Examples of cell shape among unicellular organisms.

rubber balloons. Many cells, indeed, do have a spherical structure: the eggs of many marine animals when released into the water, many yeasts and bacteria, and a variety of unicellular algae. But from the different shapes attained by other forms of unicellular life, it appears certain that the organism itself rather than surface tension or external forces exerts a dominant effect on its shape. Some bacteria are rods, spirals, and even commas; among the algae, the diatoms, desmids, and dinoflagellates, with their unusual contours and outer skeletons, take on a bizarre appearance (Fig. 7). Even the amoeba, familiar to most of you, is not normally a sphere. Generally flattened because it rests on a surface, it has no particular shape, but rather is a fluid glob of protoplasm that can flow this way or that; only at rest or in death does it round up.

One of the most remarkable single-celled organisms is *Acetabularia,* an algal form found in the warm marine waters (Fig. 8). Some species may be 9 to 10 cm in height, and a distinctive cap, characteristic of each species, tops off the whole structure. Yet until it commences its fruiting stage, it is essentially a single cell, with the nucleus residing at the base of the stalk in the rootlike *rhizoid.*

When we turn to a consideration of the cell shapes of multicellular organisms, we find that mechanical forces still determine form to some extent, but that the function a cell performs is also a factor in the shaping process. As pointed out above, free-floating cells with thin membranes tend to be spherical because this is the most economical (i.e., the smallest) shape that can confine a given mass of protoplasm. A physicist would say that the cell

Fig. 8. *Acetabularia,* the green alga that grows in warm marine waters. It is unicellular until it enters a reproductive stage, at which time the cap divides into reproductive cells. (Copyright by General Biological Supply House, Inc., Chicago.)

is obeying the *law of minimal surfaces.* When spherical cells are packed together, however, they tend to become faceted as they come in contact with neighboring cells, much as the sides of soap bubbles become flattened when the bubbles are jammed together in a small space. In animals this

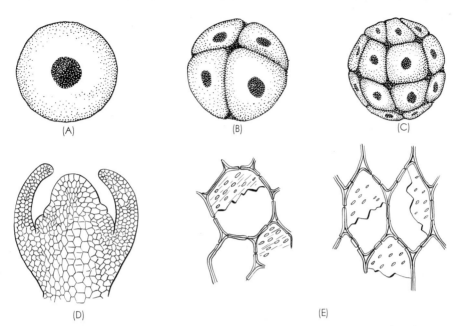

Fig. 9. The accommodation of cells in a given area requires that shape be modified if close packing is to be achieved. (A) Fertilized egg of a snail; (B) 4-cell stage of developing snail embryo; (C) 16-cell stage of the same snail, with no increase in the size of the embryo over that in (A) and (B); (D) Typical apical growing region of a plant; (E) Cells in the pith of an elderberry in cross section (left) and longitudinal section (right). Both sectional and surface faces of cell walls of the elderberry show openings (pits) between cells.

phenomenon can best be seen in the early stages of the development of an embryo (Fig. 9). The cell mass still retains for a brief period the rounded shape and size of the original egg, but in adjusting to the available space, the cells shape themselves accordingly. Similar arrangements of plant cells can be seen in the growing tips of roots or branches, in a potato tuber, or in the central pitch of an elderberry stem.

Cells, of course, are not always packed in the same way. Some are layered in flat sheets, as in the inner linings of blood vessels. These naturally tend to have greater dimensions in lateral directions than they do in depth, since the mechanical factors of stretching force them into such a shape. Muscles and bones are also elongated structures, oriented by growth stresses; their slender cells run parallel to the organ's long axis.

It would be a mistake, however, to over-emphasize the role of mechanical forces in shaping cells, because a cell's function often determines its shape. Figure 10 illustrates four types of animal cells. The human red blood cell is spherical when viewed face on, flattened and concave when seen from the side. Its function, of course, is to transport oxygen from the lungs to the tissues, and carbon dioxide from the tissues to the lungs. Its thin dimensions permit it to exchange gases rapidly, while its rounded contours allow it to slide easily through even the smallest capillaries. A spherical cell would be useless in this respect, for the gas exchange be-

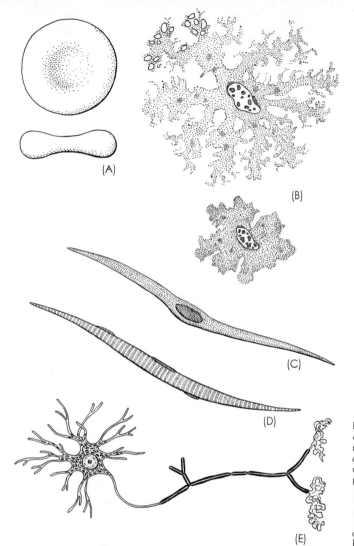

Fig. 10. Animal cells of different shapes. (A) human red blood cells, front and side view; (B) pigment-containing melanocyte, expanded and contracted; (C) smooth muscle cell; (D) striated muscle cell; (E) nerve cell, with axon (long branch) and dendrites (the finer, small branches).

tween the exterior of the cell and its center would be very slow in proportion to its size.

The three long cells in Fig. 10 are examples of muscle and nerve cells. The former contract violently when a muscle is in action, while the latter, which may reach over three feet in length in a human, is part of an extensive communication network—the telephone system, if you will—for relaying messages throughout the body. Imagine, if you can, a nerve or muscle cell having a spherical or flat shape. Would it be able to perform its function as efficiently?

The last two cells in Fig. 10 are *melanocytes*, so-called because they contain a black pigment, *melanin*, that is responsible for the dark color in the skins of animals. It can exist in either form, and can transform itself from one to the other as the occasion demands. When the melanocytes are contracted, an animal such as the chameleon or flounder will appear light; when expanded, with its branches extended, the animal appears darker. The melanocyte, therefore, not only gives color to the skin but also provides protective coloration that enables the animal to blend into either a light or a dark background. No other shape of cell could perform this function so well.

Figure 11 shows a number of cell shapes from various parts of a plant. As the legend indicates, each type has a special function, and it requires but little imagination to see that the particular shape adopted is ideal for the particular purpose of each cell.

We find, therefore, that the shapes of cells are related both to the body plan of the organism and to the varied activities the organism performs in order to live. Plants and animals differ principally in their mobility and mode of nutrition. A plant, of course, is not adapted for motion. Except when free-floating, it generally has devices for anchorage and for the absorption of water and mineral salts (roots), for the conduction of substances through the system (stem and veins of leaves), for the manufacture of food through photosynthesis (leaves), and for reproduc-

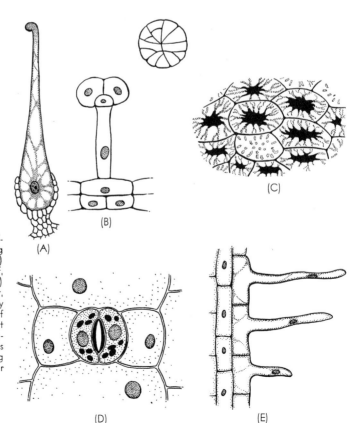

Fig. 11. Plant cells of different shapes. (A) Stinging hair cell of a nettle; (B) Glandular hair of a leaf, side and top view; (C) Dead cells in a peach pit, showing the extremely heavy walls; (D) Pair of guard cells in a leaf that enclose the stomatal openings through which gases pass; (E) Root hairs arising from the epidermis, or outer layer.

tion (flowers or other reproductive organs). Animals, however, must search for their food, and must have a bodily construction designed for this purpose, with structures for support (bones, cartilage, or exo-skeleton as in the lobster), for movement (muscles), for communication (nerves), and for digestion, excretion, secretion, circulation, and reproduction. Since the cell is the living brick in all these structures, we naturally conclude that it is an extraordinarily flexible unit, capable of adapting to the situation it finds itself in and to the function it must perform.

Cell Size

The size of cells, like their shape, varies widely, as we can see if we choose cells at random from the plant and animal kingdoms. The smallest cells are found in the bacteria (0.2–5.0 μ), and lie just at the limits of resolution of the light microscope. The largest is the egg of the ostrich, which measures about 6 inches around the outside and about 3 inches (75 mm) when the shell is removed. The ratio of the linear dimensions between the largest and smallest cells is about 75,000:1; the ratio of their volumes is about $75,000^3:1$. The order of difference is the same as that between a sphere one inch in diameter and one that is more than a mile wide.

The range of cell size in the human body extends from the semi-spherical *small leucocyte* (white blood cell), having a diameter of 3–4 μ, to the nerve cell, the axon of which may be over three feet in length. In inches, the range is 3/25,000 to 36, or a ratio of 1:300,000 for the longest dimension. Such a comparison is misleading, however, for the main body of the nerve cell (Fig. 10) is not nearly so different in size (100 μ) from that of the small leucocyte. The ratio, in fact, when computed on this basis, is about 30:1, but even this comparison has little meaning without a consideration of the factors governing size. A hen's egg, for instance, with outside dimensions of 60 x 45 mm, is large because it stores food in an enormous yolk for the developing embryo; a human embryo, on the other hand, draws its nutrients from its mother so the egg (0.1 mm) has little need for a reserve of food. Nerve, muscle, and blood cells have different sizes because of the particular tasks they do. With cells of similar function, we find that three factors tend to govern size: (1) the nucleo-cytoplasmic ratio, (2) the ratio of cell surface area to cell volume, and (3) the rate of cellular activity or metabolism. Although these factors are obviously interrelated, since each involves surface-area considerations, for convenience we will consider them separately.

We have already mentioned that the nucleus is the controlling center of the cell. In cooperation with the cytoplasm, the nucleus regulates the growth, development, and continued existence of the cell, and although a cell can function for a time without a nucleus, the cytoplasm will soon become like an assembly production line without a policy-making board of directors and cease to operate. The nucleus, however, cannot extend its control over an indefinitely large amount of cytoplasm because as the cell enlarges, the surface area of the nucleus, across which an interchange of materials must pass, increases only as the square of the cell radius (area of a sphere $= 4\pi r^2$), while the cell volume increases as the cube (volume $= \frac{4}{3} \pi r^3$) (Fig. 12). A disproportionate increase of cytoplasm would soon put the cell out of metabolic kilter. The nucleus can increase its surface area by changing its shape, or by doubling its volume by doubling the number of its *chromosomes,* the main components of the nucleus. In our analogy, each member of the board of directors would become more efficient or the number of board members would be doubled. Most mature cells, however, maintain a relatively constant nucleo-cytoplasmic ratio, while growing cells divide to keep the ratio below a certain maximum value.

The second limitation in a cell's size is the amount of its surface area. Metabolism, of course, occurs continuously throughout the entire cell mass, but the substances required for metabolism can only pass in and out of the cells through the surface membranes. Oxygen, for example, is required by virtually all cells. If sufficient oxygen is to reach the center of the cell, its concentration outside the cell has to be at or above a certain critical value. This value is determined by the ease with which oxygen passes into the cell, the rate at which it is used per unit quantity of protoplasm, and the cell's dimensions. An equation can be set up to express this relationship; in it, the rate of utilization of oxygen and its diffusibility are in terms of simple proportionality, while cell size or area is expressed as a squared value. Therefore, if the radius of a cell is doubled, the area of the cell will be the square of this value. Consequently, if air, which contains 20 per cent oxygen, just supplies the center of a cell 0.1 mm in diameter with sufficient oxygen to keep it metabolizing normally, it would take pure oxygen to supply a similar flow to a cell having a diameter of 0.23 mm. For an increase in diameter of $\sqrt{5}$, then, a cell must receive 5 times the amount of oxygen at its outer boundary.

The surface of the cell is as important in controlling the outgoing flow as it is in regulating the intake of necessary gases, water, and foods. And since the surface area increases by the square of the radius and the volume increases as its cube (Fig. 12), the volume is governed by the ability of the surface to provide the interior with the necessities demanded of it in metabolism; if the volume is too large, the center cannot function properly. These limitations can, however, be overcome in a variety of ways. The cells can abandon their spherical shape by flattening, folding,

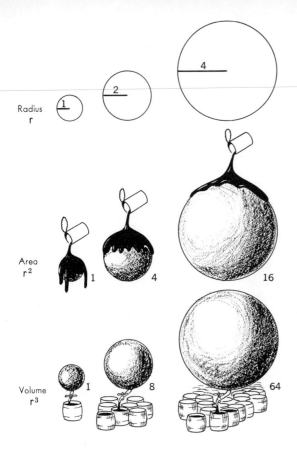

Fig. 12. As the cell increases in size, the area increases as the square of the radius, and the volume increases as the cube of the radius. Assuming the cell to be a sphere, and that its radius increases from 1:2:4, we see that the appropriate area ratios will be 1:4:16, and the appropriate volume ratios will be 1:8:64.

or elongating to increase their surface area without increasing their bulk. Having increased the area of their surface, and thus having increased the amount of nutrient that will be able to flow in and out, they can consequently enlarge their dimensions and still not interfere with metabolic rates, as long as the expansion does not result in a drastic alteration of the nucleocytoplasmic ratio.

The surface-volume dilemma appears over and over again in living organisms, and it is met and solved in various

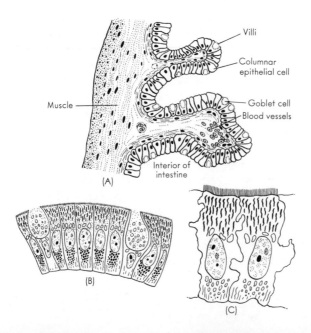

Fig. 13. The arrangement of cells in the small intestine of the human illustrates how the distribution increases the absorptive area. (A) A section through the convoluted surface, showing two of the projections or villi; (B) A detailed drawing of the surface to show both the columnar cells and the goblet cells which secrete mucus; (C) Columnar cells, showing their irregular contact area and the brush border at their outer, absorptive surface.

ways. A nerve cell, for example, may reach a yard in length, although the cell body may not be especially large, and the tenuousness of the axons and dendrites is such as to present no problem for the rapid exchange of materials across their surfaces. For the cells that cannot reach larger proportions, however, an increase in number rather than size is the only solution. An organ of the body (as opposed to a single cell) has more elaborate means to meet the demands assigned to it. In mammals, for example, the digestive system is a long coiled tube, and its inner absorptive lining is composed of many convoluted (folded) surfaces made up of small columnar or cuboidal cells arranged much as is the piling on a bath towel (Fig. 13). The inner surface of the lungs is also designed to facilitate the rapid exchange of oxygen and carbon dioxide; each cell is in contact with a blood vessel on one side and air on the other.

A plant that is large with respect to its surface area can increase that area by spreading out leaves and by sprouting roots with thousands of root hairs on them that provide an enormous surface for absorption. A grown beech tree in an open field, for example, will have as many as 200,000 leaves, with an exposed surface area of 4,500,000 cm². The individual plant cell, however, meets the surface-volume problem in yet another way—by developing a large vacuole filled with cell liquids in the center of the cell (Fig. 14). This pushes the cytoplasm to the outside of a very large cell so that a rapid exchange of materials is possible.

The third factor that affects the size of a cell is the rate of activity carried on inside it. Although cell size is not absolutely correlated

Fig. 14. Three examples of plant cells, illustrating the manner by which the formation of a vacuole pushes the cytoplasm to the outside, thus increasing the exchange of materials between the cytoplasm and the exterior of the cell. (A) Cells from the one-cell-thick skin in an onion bulb; (B) Cell from the stamen hair of the spiderwort, *Tradescantia*; (C) Typical cell of a leaf, showing the plastids, nucleus, and cytoplasm forced to the outside. Strands of cytoplasm may often cross through the vacuole, as shown in (B).

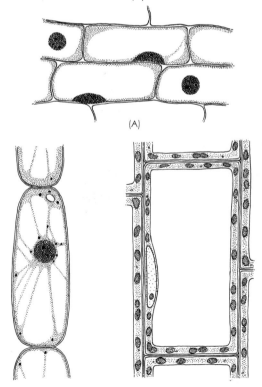

(A)

(B)   (C)

with metabolism, the rapidly metabolizing cells of such organisms as bacteria, hummingbirds, shrews, bees, flies, and mosquitoes are generally smaller than those of the more slowly metabolizing animals such as man, elephants, amphibians (frogs, toads, etc.), and grasshoppers. The surface exchanges in the cells of the smaller, more active animals must be accomplished in a more rapid fashion, and the cells must thus be smaller so that the amount of surface area relative to volume can be at a maximum. If this were not the case, the metabolic processes would bog down. For example, if the elephant metabolized at the same rate as the hummingbird, it would roast itself, because the tremendous amount of heat it would

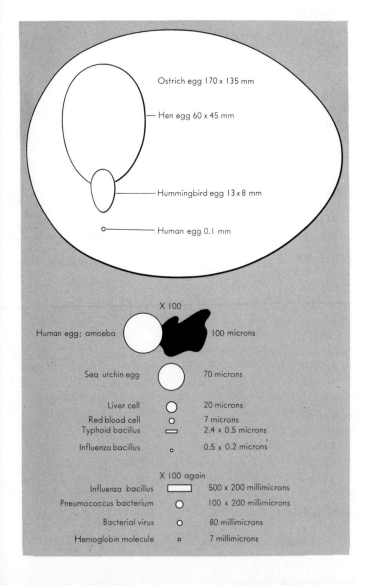

Ostrich egg 170 x 135 mm

Hen egg 60 x 45 mm

Hummingbird egg 13 x 8 mm

Human egg 0.1 mm

X 100

Human egg; amoeba   100 microns

Sea urchin egg   70 microns

Liver cell   20 microns
Red blood cell   7 microns
Typhoid bacillus   2.4 x 0.5 microns

Influenza bacillus   0.5 x 0.2 microns

X 100 again

Influenza bacillus   500 x 200 millimicrons
Pneumococcus bacterium   100 x 200 millimicrons

Bacterial virus   80 millimicrons

Hemoglobin molecule   7 millimicrons

Fig. 15. A scale of sizes of different kinds of cells, with the bacterial virus and the hemoglobin molecule included for comparative purposes. The ostrich egg and the eggs within it are here reduced by one-half.

generate could not escape. The same result would occur if a human egg cell metabolized at the same rate as a small bacterial cell.

Cell size can also be viewed as a problem in structural engineering. Protoplasm is a viscous substance that needs a support of some kind to keep it together and functioning as it should. Units of it are thus confined within the area of the cell by membranes of 0.1 μ or less in thickness that form the elastic but firm walls of the cell. Since cells of minute dimensions would make inefficient use of this support, and oversize cells, because of internal pressure, would burst like punctured balloons, a balance must be maintained between the need for support and the need for a proper surface-volume relationship.

What, then, is the optimum size of a cell that will enable it to perform its duties most efficiently? Obviously there is no simple answer. Figure 15 places a number of different cells on a graded scale of size, and since each of these cells exists we must assume that it is efficient. If we exclude eggs from our consideration—they really belong in a category by themselves—we find that the maximum diameter is about 100 μ, while the minimum is approximately 0.1 μ, a ratio of 1,000:1. (We have also excluded viruses because, whether they are cells or not, their energy for metabolism comes from the cell they have parasitized.) It is quite unlikely, however, that the rates of activity between the most active and the least active cells is of the same magnitude. Probably it is no more than 100:1, since cell diameter varies as the square of metabolism (see p. 19 for a discussion of the oxygen relationships). But this is an area in which good comparative studies are lacking, although now that tissue culture techniques have been perfected it should be possible to compute such rates with relative ease.

Cell Number

Let us now turn to a brief consideration of the number of cells found within any given organism. This number may seem impossible to calculate in so large an organism as man, but since cells are roughly the same size, simple arithmetic can give us a fairly good estimate even for large animals. The difference between a human dwarf and a giant is primarily a matter of cell number rather than of size, and, generally speaking, within any one species the larger the organism the greater is the number of cells in its body.

Among unicellular forms, the cell and the organism are one and the same. Most multicellular organisms consist of an indefinite number of cells, but in a few the number is fixed. The green alga, *Pandorina morum*, found in most fresh-water ponds, is a plate made up of 8 or 16 cells; a

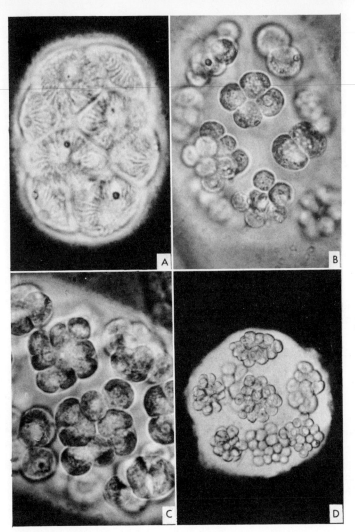

Fig. 16. Colonies of *Pandorina morum.* (A) A 16-cell colony, but with only 8 cells visible. The flagellae cannot be seen, but the dark eye spots indicate that the bottom of the colony is its anterior end. (B) Vegetative reproduction, with the cells of the original colony dividing to form new colonies; 2-celled and 4-celled stages are visible. (C) 8-celled stages. (D) 16-celled stages; these will be released from the confines of the old colony to become independent. (Courtesy of Dr. Annette W. Coleman.)

similar and related species, *P. charkowiensis,* consists of either 16 or 32 cells; no intermediate cell numbers are found. When new colonies are formed in *P. morum,* each of the 16 cells divides four times to produce 16 new colonies, each with 16 cells apiece (Fig. 16). *Eudorina,* a related genus, may have 16, 32, or 64 cells in each .colony, the sequence of numbers being regulated by the fact that all cells divide simultaneously. Such definite cell numbers are found in only a few of the animal forms.

Most organisms, however, consist of an indefinite number of cells, limited only by the ultimate size the organism attains at maturity. Suppose we take man as an example. During the first 285 days of his life, that is, the gestation period, man grows from a single egg cell that divides again and again to form a newborn infant weighing about seven pounds. The egg cell weighed about one-millionth of an ounce at conception, but at birth the infant consists of 2,000,000,000,000 cells. If all the cells divided at equal rates, this number of cells would have been reached at the end of 42 cell generations, and each cell would have divided once every 6.8 days. At maturity the average human male, weighing about 160 lb, consists of about 60 thousand billion cells.

Not all cells, however, divide at the same rate and for the same duration of time. Some reach maturity and stop dividing long before others; some continue to divide until death intervenes. The development of the human form, therefore, involves many things; an increase in cell number is but one of these. For example, at birth all of the nerve and muscle cells are formed. The destruction of any one of these cells would be an irretrievable loss, for they no longer possess the capacity to multiply. They are not fully formed, however, for they must elongate and enlarge to reach mature proportions. There is some, though not much, cell multiplication in the liver and kidney, but the loss of a part of these organs would cause a marked rise in the rate of cell multiplication as the body attempted to bring the organ back to its normal size. On the other hand, the blood cells are continually being produced and as continually being lost through death; they wear out in the process of maintaining the proper balance of oxygen and carbon dioxide in the body. The cells of the cornea of the eye and of the skin are also constantly being worn away and replaced by the cells from underneath the surface. In humans, the number and replacement rate of the reproductive cells vary in the two sexes. In the female, at birth there are about 400,000 *follicles* (germ cells); these do not increase in number, but rather decrease as the female ages. Since the eggs are shed monthly for a period of about thirty years, only about 400 eggs mature. The remainder degenerate and disappear. In the male, however, sperm cells are continually produced from puberty to senility, when the germinal tissue atrophies. During the period of active sexual life, the daily production of sperm amounts to millions of cells. Many other vertebrate animals, on the other hand, have definite breeding seasons, and their sexual cells are produced only at those times.

3 The Structure of Cells

It is impossible to imagine any biological activity that does not involve a chemical reaction. Breathing, walking, seeing, tasting, even just existing, requires energy. This energy, in turn, is derived from chemical reactions that take place within cells.

The cell, therefore, can be considered as a chemical factory. It may, of course, be a general-purpose factory, capable of performing all the services and of manufacturing all the products necessary to continue life; this must obviously be true in unicellular organisms. Or it may be a speciality shop, doing only a single job, such as serving as nerve cells for communication or as muscle cells for movement. Regardless of its nature, however, a cell, like a factory, must possess a certain organization in order to be efficient; it must contain a controlling or directing center, a source of supplies, a source of energy, and the machinery for making its product or performing its service. It is not surprising, then, that cells, despite their great variety of shapes, sizes, and functions, share many common features. If a cell becomes specialized, we might expect to find a change in organization and, possibly, the appearance of new parts but not at the sacrifice of basic features. For this reason, the biologist considers that *form and function are inseparable biological phenomena;* to express it in another way, an organized activity is associated with an organized arrangement of parts.

26

Just as there is no typical plant or animal, there is no cell that we can designate as a typical or generalized cell that is representative of all cells. Each cell, or cell type, is more or less unique. For purposes of orientation, however, we can construct a "composite" cell having many of the features we wish to discuss. Figure 6 is such a cell, seen as it would appear in the phase-contrast microscope. The cell surface is bounded by a *cell* or *plasma membrane*. This is the living outer boundary in all cells, but plant cells generally have an additional wall, exterior to the membrane and of variable composition, which serves for support. All materials coming into the cell must enter through the membrane and the wall. In the center of the cell is the *nucleus*. It is the controlling center of the cell but it is also capable of limited synthesis and has at least part of its own power supply. The remainder of the cell is the *cytoplasm,* the main portion of the cell, which has a source of energy and contains various subunits that perform needed tasks. We still lack many pieces of information about the coordinated behavior of this cellular factory, but at least the major features are reasonably clear.

The Cellular Boundary

Although we recognize that a membrane forms the outer boundary of all cells, we know surprisingly little about its structure. As indicated above, it is a living portion of the cell and the screen through which all substances taken into the cell must pass; it is elastic and pliable in some cells, quite rigid and unyielding in others; and it is capable of limited repair if punctured by a needle. It must also be capable of growth as the cell enlarges.

The cell membrane is not easily seen in the light microscope, but the electron microscope usually shows it to be double-layered. It is generally assumed that a double layer of lipid (fat) molecules is sandwiched between two protein layers. The protein layers would account for the fact that the membrane is elastic, since the long protein molecules can fold or unfold with relative ease. The lipid layers are suggested by the observation that fat solvents readily penetrate the membrane and enter the cell.

The membrane is also said to be *semi-permeable,* i.e., it permits the entry of some molecules into the cell but not others. Virtually all biological membranes possess this characteristic. Amino acids (the building blocks of proteins) and glucose pass more easily through the membrane than do many other smaller molecules; size of molecule, therefore, does not always determine ease of passage. Potassium moves across the membrane rapidly and can accumulate in the cell; sodium cannot. Water diffuses easily in or out of the cell, depending on whether solutions exterior to the cell are hypotonic or hypertonic. From these few examples of molecular movement across membranes, and from the further fact that the permeability of a membrane is not fixed and constant but rather is subject to change from one moment to the next, it not only appears that the structure of the membrane and the size and character of the entering molecules are important considerations, but also that the cell itself can determine the behavior of the membrane. How it does this we do not know for certain.

The cell membrane, therefore, not only provides mechanical support and exterior form for our cellular factory, it also is very much a part of the living machinery of the cell. The same cannot be said of the cell wall of a plant. Secreted by the cell and serving as a skeletal framework, it is nonliving. The oldest part of the wall is on the outside; the most recently formed portion lies adjacent to the active cytoplasm. The chief structural component is *cellulose,* a characteristic plant substance formed from sugars that has the general formula $(C_6H_{10}O_5)_n$.

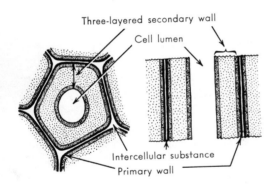

Three-layered secondary wall

Cell lumen

Intercellular substance

Primary wall

Fig. 17. Typical wall structure of matured and lignified plant cells. Left, cross section showing arrangement of the various layers and the complex structure of the secondary wall; right, longitudinal section through a similar cell. (Reprinted with permission from K. Esau, *Plant Anatomy.* New York: Wiley, 1953.)

Figure 17 illustrates the wall of a typical plant cell. Shared by adjacent cells is a layer known as the *middle lamella.* It forms the first partition between two cells as they arise through cell division and acts as an *intercellular cement* binding cells together. It consists mostly of *pectin,* a substance related to cellulose since it is also formed from sugars, and is known to most of us as the additive responsible for the "setting" of jellies. The *primary wall,* just outside the middle lamella, is the first secretion product of the cytoplasm. While the cell is enlarging, this wall is very thin, elastic, and capable of great extension. It consists principally of celluloses and sugars of various kinds, and thickens only after the cell has ceased to enlarge. The *secondary wall* on the outside of the cell then forms. It may be thick or thin and consist of varying degrees of hardness or color. It is the part of the cell which gives various woods and plant fibers (cotton, flax, hemp) their particular character, and from which is derived the cellulose used in the manufacture of rayon, nitrocellulose, cellophane, and certain plastics.

Let us examine the growth of the cotton fiber in order to illustrate the principles of cell-wall formation. The mature fiber, or *lint* as it is called, is a single cell which may be one-half to one and one-half inches in length. Located in the outermost layer of cells, or *epidermis,* of the seed coat (Fig. 18), the lint cell is attached to neighboring cells by a middle lamella and possesses a thin primary wall. On the day of flowering, the cell begins to elongate, a process that takes 13 to 20 days and that creates a cell 1,000 to 3,000 times as long as it is wide. The primary wall then ceases to elongate, and the secondary wall forms as sugars in the cytoplasm are converted into cellulose and deposited on the inside of the primary wall. Deposition continues until the fruit is mature. The cell then dies, collapses, and flattens to give the fiber used in the manufacture of cotton threads and cloths.

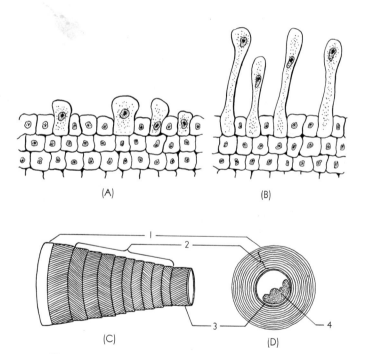

Fig. 18. Growth and structure of the cotton fiber. (A) Outer layer of cells of the young cotton seed showing the beginning enlargement of the fibers on the day of flowering; (B) Same, 24 hours later; (C) Diagram illustrating the various layers of cellulose laid down in a mature cotton fiber: (1) outer primary cell wall, (2) concentric inner layers revealing the different orientation of the cellulose in the secondary thickenings, (3) last inner layer of the secondary wall; (D) Same, in cross section, with (4) representing the remains of the cell contents. (Redrawn and modified from Brown and Ware, *Cotton,* 3rd ed. New York: McGraw-Hill, 1958.)

The formation of cellulose and its incorporation into a supporting structure illustrate two principles. In the first place, cellulose is a *macromolecule*, i.e., a long chain structure of high molecular weight, built up of repeating units of sugar (glucose) into a *crystal lattice* which eventually reaches visible proportions. In cross section, the cotton fiber has an area of about 300 μ^2 made up of approximately a billion cellulose chains. These are grouped into *fibrils* of several orders of magnitude, with each one running the length of the entire fiber in a parallel but helical fashion. The spaces between the fibrils give the fiber its flexibility and allow for the complete penetration of dyes, while the orientation of the fibrils accounts for its great tensile strength (nearly that of steel). It has been estimated that each cotton fiber contains about 10 trillion cellulose molecules, which are built up from approximately 60 quadrillion glucose molecules. A single fiber is but one of many thousand growing on the surface of each cotton seed, and each glucose molecule must be manufactured by the cell. From these rough calculations, we can gain some appreciation of the activity of the plant cells in transforming carbon dioxide and water through photosynthesis into an organic molecule; multiplying these molecules, the cell then builds them into an elaborate structure, the cell wall. The process of repetition of molecules is used by the cell to form its elements of structure—proteins, fats, nucleic acids, and polysaccharides—in much the same way that man does to form plastics and synthetic fibers.

Secondly, the organization of the cell wall illustrates two sound construction principles. The cotton fiber is pure cellulose, and its strength is gained by grouping the molecules into larger and larger fibrils; this structure is the basis of cable and rope construction. Other types of cell walls, however, are impregnated with different substances. One of these is *lignin*, a complex sugar derivative which tends to form in the spaces between the cellulose fibrils. This arrangement is also the principle of the reinforced concrete that is utilized in many of our modern buildings; the cellulose provides rods of high tensile strength and the lignin is a substance that is resistant to pressures. The cellulose need not, of course, be as well oriented as in the cotton fiber, and other substances such as *cutin* and *waxes*, both derivatives of fatty acids, may replace lignin. In such instances, the strength of the wall is lessened.

Growth of the cell wall is by *apposition* and *intussusception*. In the first process, materials are laid down on the surface of earlier-formed walls. If the daily additions are of different densities, a laminated appearance results. The cotton fiber is formed in this way. But when lignin is inserted between the cellulose fibers, as it is in most woody cells, the process is called intussusception, which means the addition of new molecules among those already present.

The Controlling Center

The most prominent feature of a cell, when viewed under the microscope, is the *nucleus*. It is the controlling center, the board of directors
of our cellular factory, for in it are found the *chromosomes* and the *genes*
which somehow guide and determine the character, activities, and destiny
of each individual cell. In the next two chapters we shall deal with the
behavior and structure of chromosomes during cell division when they
are most visibly prominent; here we concern ourselves with nuclear appearance, chemistry and function.

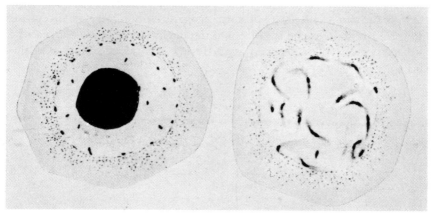

Fig. 19. Cells of the watermelon, *Citrullus vulgaris*. Left, cell in interphase
with a large nucleolus and numerous small chromocenters. Right, same cell
in prophase with the nucleolus gone and the chromocenters showing up as
the heterochromatic parts of individual chromosomes. (L. Geitler, *Chromo-
somenbau*, Berlin: Gebrüder Borntraeger, 1938, after Doutreligne.)

Figure 19 illustrates two cells of the watermelon. Although not distinctly visible, each nucleus is bounded on the outside by a *nuclear membrane,* which, so far as we know, is quite similar to the cell membrane,
since it, too, is a double-layered structure made of proteins and lipids. The
main mass of the nucleus in a stained cell is seen as a fine network of
threads, beaded with coarser granules. This is the *chromatin,* which, during cell division, will become more distinctly visible as a definite number
of individual chromosomes. The network can be stained readily with basic
dyes such as *haematoxylin, carmine,* and *crystal violet,* but is generally
invisible in a living cell. The coarser chromatin granules are known as

chromocenters and consist of a type of chromatin that stains darker than the network. Recognizable, also, are one or more rounded bodies, the *nucleoli* (singular, *nucleolus*). Each nucleus possesses a definite number of nucleoli—e.g., the onion cell has four, as has man—but these sometimes fuse to form a smaller number of larger nucleoli. Let us examine each of these structures in detail.

Chromatin is the hereditary material of the cell. The fertilized egg divides again and again, and the mass of cells is molded into a man, a cow, an oak tree, or a daisy, depending on the chromatin in each cell. And, in addition, chromatin places the stamp of uniqueness upon each individual organism as well as upon each species. This has been beautifully demonstrated in *Acetabularia* (Fig. 8) by the German biologist, Hämmerling.

Two species of *Acetabularia* differ in the shape of their caps (Fig. 20). If the cap is cut off, it will form again as before, but it is also possible to graft the stalk of one species onto the nucleus-containing *rhizoid* of the other species. When the cap again forms, it is always characteristic of

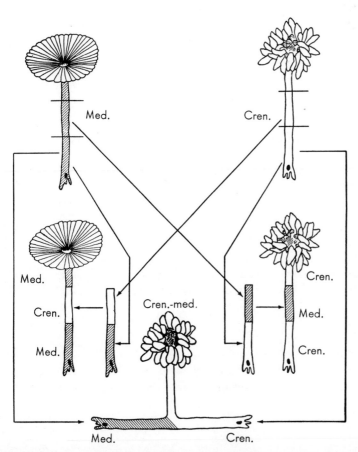

Fig. 20. Influence of the nucleus on development in *Acetabularia.* Stalk segments of *A. mediterranea* grafted onto nucleus-containing rhizoids of *A crenulata*, and vice versa, produce caps characteristic of the species contributing the nucleus. When two nucleus-containing rhizoids are grafted together, the cap consists of loose rays, as in *A. crenulata*, but their points are more rounded, as in *A. mediterranea*. (From Hämmerling.)

the nucleus and not of the grafted stalk. When both nuclei are present, the cap is intermediate in shape, reflecting the influence of each nucleus. The nucleus, therefore, causes the rest of the cell to do as it dictates.

What determines the hereditary powers of the chromatin? *Genetics,* the science of heredity, informs us that the genes carried in the chromosomes are responsible for the determination of characters. It should be possible, therefore, to analyze the chromatin chemically and so gain some idea of the molecular basis of heredity. Such an experiment has been done, and it appears that chromatin resolves itself into four major molecules: *histone,* a low-molecular-weight (c. 2,000) protein; a more *complex protein* that is distinguishable from histone; *deoxyribose nucleic acid* (DNA); and *ribose nucleic acid* (RNA). These four molecules are somehow organized together to form chromatin, but a long series of studies have demonstrated that DNA is the key molecule whose structure confers hereditary uniqueness on the cell and the individual.

In *Pneumococcus,* the bacterium responsible for some kinds of pneumonia, several strains or types are known which differ principally in the capsular (outside) material surrounding each cell. When DNA is extracted from Type I and prepared in highly purified form, it can be added to a solution containing cells of Type II. The Type I DNA is taken up by the cells of Type II, some of which thereafter are permanently transformed into Type I. These transformed cells have been shown to have part of their Type II chromatin (genes) replaced by that from Type I. No other molecule can do this, so we can only conclude that DNA is the hereditary material of the cell. Other less direct information strongly supports this conclusion. The proteins and RNA are necessary for the functioning of the nucleus, but are apparently only accessory from an hereditary point of view.

It should be pointed out that some plant viruses have RNA but no DNA in their structure. In these instances, RNA must be considered the hereditary molecule.

What then is DNA? Chemical analysis reveals it to be a compound of high molecular weight (over 1,000,000) that is made up of a number of smaller molecules linked together. These molecules include a sugar, *deoxyribose, phosphoric acid,* and four bases of which two are *pyrimidines* (*thymine* and *cytosine*) and two are purines (*adenine* and *guanine*). The chemical structure of each base is given in Fig. 21. The alternating sugar and phosphate arrangement forms the outside boundaries of DNA, while base pairs link the two sides together. The base pairs, however, are not at random, for adenine and thymine are always paired, as are guanine and cytosine. Hydrogen bonds tie the bases to each other. X-ray analysis of the molecular arrangement reveals that DNA is not a flat structure, as

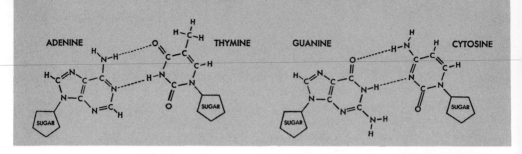

Fig. 21. Chemical configurations of the four bases found in the DNA molecule, arranged in two of the several possible configurations. Thymine and cytosine are pyrimidines; adenine and guanine are purines.

one might suspect, but a double helix, i.e., a sort of "spiral staircase" with alternating sugar-phosphate "bannisters" and "steps" of base pairs (Fig. 22). This is the Watson-Crick model of DNA, so named after its discoverers.

The DNA molecule may have thousands of turns in its spiral configuration, and the "steps" can be arranged in any order. The possible variations, therefore, are astronomical in number and give an infinite variety to the molecule. Since the DNA, in some undetermined manner, appears to be responsible for the formation of proteins and RNA, it is believed that the sequence of base pairs is the key to the heredity-determining qualities of DNA. These act apparently as a pattern or *template* to initiate the formation of other complex molecules that make up the living cell and give it its uniqueness. We can also look upon the base pairs as the letters in a genetic alphabet, which when put together in a particular sequence yield a "word" which has meaning to the cell and tells it what to do. We do not know, however, how many base pairs make up a gene or, indeed, if the number is variable or constant.

The remaining structure in the nucleus is the nucleolus. It is formed by a particular chromosome at a region known as the *nucleolar organizer*, and analysis reveals it to be made up of RNA and proteins. The function of the nucleolus, other than to manufacture proteins, is not known, but since it disappears during cell division (see Chapter 4), it may provide a means of passing genetic information and materials from the nucleus to the cytoplasm. This problem will be considered in more detail later in this chapter.

The Cellular Assembly Line

It is not entirely correct to speak of the cytoplasm as that portion of the cell concerned solely with production. Nuclei, of course, must carry on the chemical activities necessary for their own maintenance and repro-

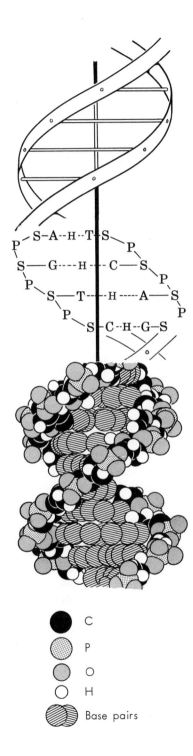

duction, and cell membranes, particularly in bacterial species, are believed to be capable of limited synthesis of substances. The cytoplasm, however, is the main assembly line of the cell, and its output is either a *product* (e.g., a secretion, storage material such as fat or starch, a pigment, or even new cells) or a *service* (e.g., CO_2–O_2 transport, message transmission, protection, or movement), or a combination of the two. To do these things, the cytoplasm requires a source of raw materials, a source of power, the machinery necessary to do the job, and mechanisms for distributing its product or service.

The raw materials needed by the cell pass into it through the plasma membrane from the outside environment. For our purposes here, we need only assume that the living organism must have these raw materials at hand, together with a source of energy, in order to transform them into living matter. The raw materials are the needed *nutrients* of an organism, and the chemical reactions utilizing these materials are its *metabolism*. Each organism and, indeed, each kind of cell has its own characteristic nutrition and metabolism.

The sun is the ultimate source of all energy needed for the main-

Fig. 22. The helix of DNA, with three different ways of representing the molecular arrangement. Top, general picture of the double helix, with the phosphate-sugar combinations making up the outside spirals and the base pairs the cross-bars; middle, a somewhat more detailed representation: phosphate (P), sugar (S), adenine (A) thymine (T), guanine (G), cytosine (C), and hydrogen (H); bottom, detailed structure showing how the space is filled with atoms: carbon (C), oxygen (O), hydrogen (H), phosphorus (P) and the base pairs.

tenance and continuation of life. Since only green plants and certain microorganisms, through the process of *photosynthesis,* can use the radiant energy of sunlight directly, it is clear that the energy must be stored in some form and then made available to the organism on demand. The energy is stored in the form of chemical energy, and the larger the molecule (e.g., fats and starches) the greater, in general, is its stored energy. Living substance, therefore, contains more chemical energy than do the raw materials from which it was made and the waste products to which it will eventually be decomposed.

The principal intake of radiant energy occurs in plants during the process of photosynthesis. Animals, however, do not photosynthesize, so in addition to taking in raw materials they must also take in energy already bound in chemical form. Once available, the energy can be transferred, stored, or utilized to do work; these processes, which are the subject of another monograph [1] in this series, are carried out under the control of cellular catalysts, or *enzymes,* so that the energy is made available only as needed instead of being rapidly burned and dissipated as heat.

The structure in the cytoplasm in which radiant energy is absorbed is the *chloroplast,* which contains the green pigment, *chlorophyll* (certain microorganisms have other light-absorbing pigments that perform the same function). Their shapes and number vary according to the particular species of plant as well as to the particular tissue; they may be absent from those cells not concerned with photosynthesis. In other tissues, such as the potato tuber, the *plastid,* as these structures are sometimes called, may serve as a storage depot, in which case the simple sugars that result from photosynthesis are transformed into inert, but potentially energy-rich, starch molecules.

The process of photosynthesis is very complex, requiring a whole battery of enzymes in the chloroplast to transform CO_2 and H_2O into sugar, but the internal structure of the plastid shows that the chlorophyll molecules are most efficiently disposed to carry out their task. Electron microscopy reveals that the plastid has an elaborately ordered structure, with membranous laminations arranged like stacks of coins or plywood sheets to form the *grana* (Fig. 23). Between the grana is the *stroma,* where the laminations are fewer or even absent. It appears that the chlorophyll is spread in monolayers on the layers of the grana, thus achieving an enormously increased surface area for the trapping of light energy.

The chloroplasts of higher plants appear to arise from less well-differentiated structures called *proplastids,* but the origin of these remains in doubt. The proplastids can divide to increase their number, but when

---

[1] W. D. McElroy, *Cellular Physiology and Biochemistry* (Englewood Cliffs, N.J.: Prentice-Hall, 1960).

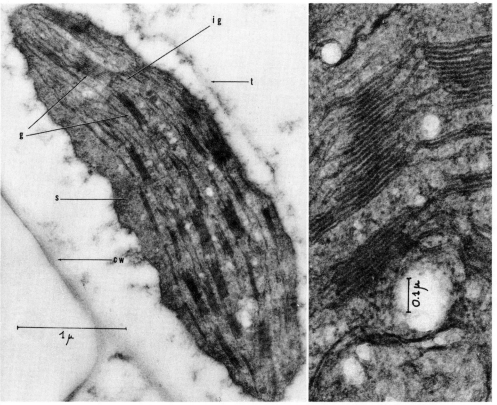

Fig. 23. Electron micrographs of a chloroplast from a spinach leaf, showing the grana (g), intergrana spaces (ig), stroma (s), membrane surrounding a vacuole (t), and the cell wall (cw). Right, a more highly magnified portion showing the distinct lamellar arrangement in the grana. (Courtesy of George Schidlofsky.)

a cell divides they are distributed more or less at random between the two daughter cells. In species such as the alga, *Spirogyra,* however, where only a single chloroplast is found, it divides synchronously with the cell. Following division, it increases to mature size.

We can, therefore, view the chloroplast as a cellular *converter* that transforms radiant energy into chemical energy which the cell can use as it needs. The whole process of photosynthesis is relatively inefficient, since most of the solar energy is dissipated as heat, but it is sufficient to sustain life as we know it.

The "powerhouse" of the cell is not the chloroplast, however, but another particle in the cytoplasm, the *mitochondrion.* It is the structure that provides the cell with most of its usable energy. Ranging in size from 0.2 to 3.0 μ and in shape from spheres to rods, mitochondria are found in virtually every type of living cell (the human red blood cell is a rare exception), where they are in constant motion. A rat liver cell of about 25 μ diameter may contain as many as 1,000 mitochondria, and wherever cellular activity is intense they tend to cluster: at the juncture where nerve cells meet and message transmission occurs, at the outer convoluted edge of intestinal cells that are actively absorbing food, and at those regions of muscle cells that are particularly concerned with contraction.

Let us first consider their structure, which has been beautifully revealed by the electron microscope (Fig. 24). A double lipo-protein membrane, similar apparently to the plasma and nuclear membranes, surrounds the individual mitochondrion. The inner membrane is thrown into many convoluted folds to provide an interior of great surface area. The outer membrane is quite elastic, and can be stretched by swelling to 100 times its normal dimensions. This suggests, of course, that the protein molecules making up the membrane can be greatly folded or extended. Substances passing in and out of the mitochondrion vary in size according to the degree of stretching of the membrane, and there is some evidence to suggest that the activity of the mitochondrion also varies as its dimension increases or decreases.

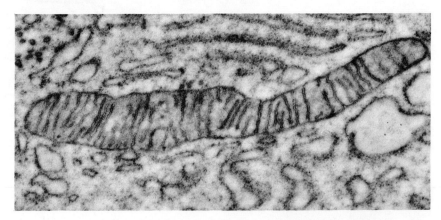

Fig. 24. Highly magnified electron micrograph of a mitochondrion in a mouse pancreatic cell. The outer boundary of the mitochondrion is a double structure, with the inner layer being continuous with the inner cross membrane (cristae). Compare the organization of the cytoplasm with that of the cells in Fig. 25. (Courtesy of Dr. Bryce L. Munger.)

In terms of function, the mitochondrion performs two important tasks. First, through a series of steps, each one of which is controlled by an enzyme, the carbohydrates, proteins, and fats are broken down into smaller and smaller molecules in a process that is accompanied by the transfer of energy. These *energy-yielding* reactions are known as *oxidations*. The energy, however, is not dissipated as heat, but rather is passed on to other molecules that contain phosphate (PO_4) where it is stored by a process of *phosphorylation* in the form of *high-energy phosphate bonds*. These are depicted as P $\sim$ P bonds, and the principal molecule in which energy is stored is *adenosine triphosphate*, or ATP. This molecule is then secreted by the mitochondrion and utilized in the cell wherever energy is needed. The mitochondrion, therefore, actively "secretes biological energy." [1]

Let us examine the entire process in more detail. The carbohydrates, proteins, and fats do not enter the mitochondrion unchanged, but are first broken down into their constituent acids before passing through the outer membrane. Inside the mitochondrion, the oxidation reactions "chip" carbon atoms from these acids (one at a time from pyruvic and amino acids, two at a time from fatty acids), until they are reduced to waste products such as CO_2 and H_2O, or to a small alcohol or acid. The energy released by the successive oxidative steps passes into ATP by the phosphorylation process. It should be emphasized that this simplified version masks a large number of reactions, each of which is governed by a particular enzyme. The mitochondrion, therefore, can be visualized as a "bag" containing all the enzymes necessary for oxidation and phosphorylation. These processes also occur outside the mitochondrion, but this structure is the principal *energy-transfer* system of the cell.

The mitochondrion can be broken into fragments by treatment with detergents, and these fragments, which are pieces of membranes, can be tested for biological activity. Part of the oxidative enzyme system is still present, so it is believed that the functional unit of the mitochondrion, i.e., the enzyme, is the same as the structural unit, the membrane. Form and function are, therefore, inseparable parts of this portion of the cell. Other enzymes of the mitochondrion, however, may well be in solution interiorly and not a part of the membranous framework at all.

In addition to energy converters (plastids) and energy transference structures (mitochondria) there are other particles in the cytoplasm. These include the *Golgi complex, vacuoles*, and *centrosomes*. (The latter, since they are concerned with cell division, will be discussed in later chapters.) The Golgi complex, also called *lipochondria*, consists of a series of membranous structures of variable shapes and dimensions whose function is not clearly understood. It has a large surface area, however, and is particularly prominent in secretory cells, and thus may well be involved in some kind of cellular synthesis; but since it has not yet been possible to isolate the complex in a pure state, its biological activity remains obscure. The Golgi complex is, however, rich in fatty (lipid) materials and readily darkens when treated with osmium or silver stains. Vacuoles, which are much more prominent in plant than in animal cells, appear simply as

[1] P. Siekevitz, "Powerhouse of the Cell," *Scientific American*, 197 (1957), 131–140.

membrane-enclosed liquid portions of the cell. Water-soluble substances, including pigments and sugars, are found in vacuoles, but except for the *contractile vacuoles* of protozoa, which eject waste products to the outside,

Fig. 25. Electron micrographs of pancreatic cells. (A) Great detail can be revealed by the electron microscope; the nucleolus is visible in the large nucleus, the endoplasmic reticulum is evident to the left and below the nucleus, and the dark spheres are zymogen granules, which eventually become transformed into an active enzyme that the cell secretes. (B) Part of a beta cell in the mouse pancreas (insulin-secreting cells); the edge of the nucleus is at the top right of the figure, and the double nature of the nuclear membrane is indicated; the cytoplasm is less well ordered than in the previous cell; each granule, which is about 0.17 micron in diameter, has its own membrane. (C) Rat pancreatic cell, showing the highly ordered endoplasmic reticulum, with the dot-like microsomes attached to the membranous reticulum. (Photos (A) and (B) courtesy of Dr. Bryce L. Munger; (C) courtesy of Dr. George Palade.)

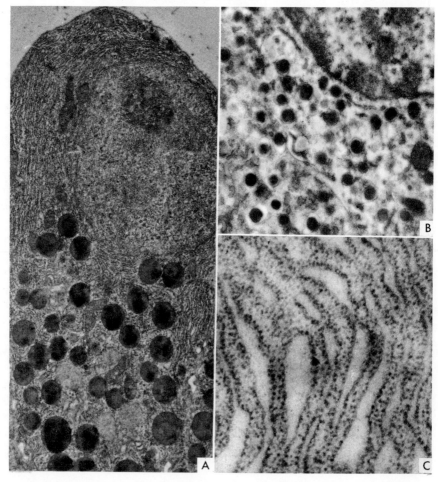

and the *food vacuoles* of other unicellular forms, which aid in digestion, their principal function is to maintain a proper internal pressure in cells.

The remainder of the cell seems to be made up of a semi-viscous fluid; a punctured cell, for example, collapses as its contents ooze out. This initial impression is deceiving, however, for electron microscopy reveals that the ground substance of the cell is as structurally compartmentalized as are the larger cellular bodies such as the nucleus and mitochondria. Figure 25 illustrates the highly ordered arrangement of membranes that make up this cellular background, which is called the *ergastoplasm* or *endoplasmic reticulum*. The membranes can be variously arranged and may, indeed, rapidly appear and disappear in dividing cells, but they form a conspicuous element in such cells as, for example, those in the liver and pancreas. Lining the membrane, or floating free in the cytoplasm when the reticulum is less evident, are numerous small, electron-dense particles which have been shown to be very rich in RNA. When cells are fragmented, the reticulum is broken up, but the fragments, which consist of pieces of membranes and particles, can be tested for biological activity. The RNA-rich particles, called *microsomes*, are particularly active in the synthesis of proteins, while the membrane itself appears to be involved in the synthesis of *steroids*, a group of compounds which include certain of the *hormones*. We therefore look upon the endoplasmic reticulum as the principal manufacturing portion of our factory, although we are far from a complete comprehension of its operation as a whole.

The Integrated Cell

An efficiently operated factory is a planned, not a haphazard, affair; its continuous operation requires, as we have pointed out, direction, power, machinery, and raw materials, and the parts must be related to the functions they perform. Nature has constructed cells along the same lines as we have constructed factories, but a dissection of the cell and its parts does not provide a complete picture of how the cell operates as a unit. However, a generalized picture is beginning to emerge.

It must be abundantly clear that the study of cells is, in essence, the study of interrelated macromolecular systems, since the three key molecules of cellular structure and function—DNA, RNA, and protein—are of giant size. They are also of infinite variety because the sequence of base pairs in the nucleic acids and of amino acids in the proteins can vary tremendously; it is this variation that determines the uniqueness of cells and individuals.

The DNA of the nucleus is the molecule of heredity that controls the cell. Its sequence of base pairs is the alphabet of life of the cell, and

provides the basic information and direction which the cell needs to perform its duties. RNA, which appears to be formed first in the nucleus but
is active principally in the microsomal part of the cytoplasm, is believed
to be the messenger that carries this information from DNA to the sites
of protein synthesis. If this is so, then each RNA molecule must possess
a particular molecular configuration in order for a particular protein to be
formed. The proteins, in turn, enter into most of the cellular structures.
Since they include among their kind all the enzymes that catalyze the
innumerable chemical reactions of the cell, they must, because of the
special tasks they perform, be the crucial pieces of machinery of our
cellular factory that determine what product it makes or what service it
renders. For example, one of the smallest proteins, *insulin,* which is
formed by certain cells in the pancreas and which controls the amount
of sugar in the blood, contains 17 different amino acids in the total of 51
that make up the molecule; if the position of any of the amino acids is
altered, the protein is no longer insulin. Yet a change in the DNA molecule can mean that no insulin is formed, and hereditary diabetes is the
result.

Similarly, a change (mutation) in a DNA molecule in the human
nucleus can change the normal *hemoglobin* of the blood to an abnormal
type that is responsible for a disease known as *sickle cell anemia.* But this
change in DNA, the nature of which is not yet known, alters only one
amino acid out of the hundreds making up the large hemoglobin molecule (Fig. 26). It is apparent, then, that our future knowledge of how

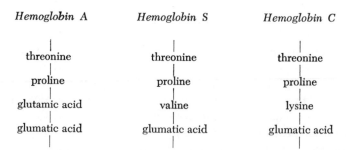

Fig. 26. Four of the hundreds of amino acids contained in a hemoglobin
molecule. A single mutation in a gene causes only the glutamic acid in
Hemoglobin A (normal) to be replaced by valine and thus changes it to
Hemoglobin S, producing sickle cell anemia; another mutation changes
the normal hemoglobin to Hemoglobin C, in which lysine occupies the
position of glutamic acid or valine. All the other amino acids remain unchanged.

cellular activity is controlled lies in a better understanding of the interactions and interrelations of DNA, RNA, and protein. Until these are
known, our insight into the behavior of cells can only be fragmentary.

William Bateson, the great English geneticist of an earlier generation, once wrote: "The greatest advance I can conceive in biology would be the discovery of the instability which leads to the continued division of the cell. When I look at a dividing cell I feel as an astronomer might do if he beheld the formation of a double star: that an original act of creation is taking place before me."

Every biologist who has ever watched a living cell divide, or visualized the process when observing stained cells, has been as fascinated as was Bateson. Indeed, without too great a stretch of the imagination, we can characterize the movements of the chromosomes, their meticulous partitioning into daughter cells, and the segmentation of the cytoplasm as an exquisite minuet. As we shall see in this and the next chapter, the paired chromatids of mitosis and the paired chromosomes of meiosis are not only the dancers; since they are the control centers of the cell, they are, collectively, the composer and conductor as well, who direct the activity of the other parts of the cell as the orchestration progresses to an end. With another cell division, the minuet commences all over again with but little variation. The meaning of the dance and the role of the dancers will become clear as we consider the cell in division in this and the next chapter.

Each of us developed from a single cell; this cell came from a preceding cell, and so on back to the beginning of cellular life. Our heritage from the past and our living extension into the future comprise a slender but unbroken series of perfectly formed, individual cells. They are perfect in the sense that, although they may vary, they are able to live, reproduce, and give rise to new cells and hence to new individuals.

The ways in which new cells originate have been extensively investigated and much debated ever since the cellular nature of organisms was realized. The cell theory, of course, formally recognized that the cell is the basic unit of biological organization and function. Yet not until the middle of the nineteenth century was it generally accepted that cells originate through the division of pre-existing cells. We attribute this idea to the German, Rudolf Virchow, who stated in 1858:

> Where a cell exists there must have been a pre-existing cell just as the animal arises only from an animal and the plant only from a plant. The principle is thus established, even though the strict proof has not yet been produced for every detail, that through the whole series of living forms, whether entire animal or plant organisms or their component parts, there are rules of eternal law and continuous development, that is, of continuous reproduction.

Although we cannot reconstruct the beginnings of life from what we know today, presumably it did not begin in the form of the cells that we now see under our microscopes. They are the products of ages of evolution. Nor can life be originated anew; it is only spawned from pre-existing life. This theory, known as *biogenesis*, we credit to Louis Pasteur, who although not particularly concerned with the reproduction of cells, first demonstrated that the spontaneous generation of life could not occur under the conditions existing on earth today. He took two flasks of broth and boiled them in such a way as to kill all the organisms in them. One flask he left open; the other he stoppered and made airtight. Within a few days the open flask contained bacteria, yeast, or molds of some sort, which, of course, were borne in the air; these germs, as we call them, under the microscope are seen to consist of cells of various sorts. The stoppered flask, however, contained no life whatsoever, and could not until air was once more admitted. Yet air could be passed through the filter without contaminating the flask provided the air was filtered of any organisms that it contained. These experiments, simple though they were, had far-reaching consequences because they disproved once and for all the idea that life can be created under present conditions; Pasteur and Virchow thus definitely established that life in a cellular form can only come from pre-existing life which also has a cellular form.

Man consists of approximately 10^{14} cells. Not only must these be formed and differentiated as the body matures, they must also be constantly replaced as they pass through their life cycle and disintegrate. In fact, within any organism that grows or requires repair, the process of cell division must produce new cells at the rate and for the period of time demanded by the organism at its particular age and in its particular environment. Not all cells, of course, divide at the same rate.

One of the most remarkable phenomena of nature, however, is the fact that in all organisms the process of cell division is essentially the same. Thus if we describe this process as it takes place in one or two kinds of cells, we can see how it operates in the whole gamut of living organisms. The drama of cell division centers largely in the nucleus, but we must not forget that the cytoplasm also undergoes a significant series of changes and that we must consider the process in its entirety before we can fully appreciate all its many aspects.

Roottip Cells in Division

The roottip of the broad bean, *Vicia faba,* provides an excellent example of a tissue in an active state of division, or *mitosis.* The chromosomes are large and few in number (12), and preparations of the dividing cells are easily made.

A panoramic view of a growing roottip can be obtained from either a longitudinal section cut on a microtome or from a squashed preparation of flattened cells. The stains employed in each case are different, and the end result varies accordingly (contrast the cells of the onion with those of the broad bean in Fig. 28). In the cells of an onion, the *nucleoli* (one to four in number) stand out sharply in the less deeply staining nucleus; these, however, are not evident in the broad bean cells, but this is due to the fact that they do not stain rather than that they are absent.

Let us now consider the stages of mitosis (Figs. 27 and 28), starting with a cell about to enter the first stage, or *interphase,* of the division cycle. The nucleus is large, when compared to nuclei in non-dividing cell tissues, and although we do not know what mechanism stimulates a cell to divide, we do know that *nucleic acids* and *proteins,* large molecules found in every nucleus, are synthesized during interphase as a preparatory step to division. There is little definable structure except for the nucleoli and *chromocenters* (see also Fig. 19), which means that the nucleic acids of the chromosomes are either too diffused to absorb much dye or are so hydrated that the dye is not accumulated in sufficient quantity to stain them intensely. The chromosomes, therefore, are not individually distinguishable in interphase.

The cell enters *prophase* when the chromosomes become visibly distinct as long thin threads. They are divided longitudinally into identical

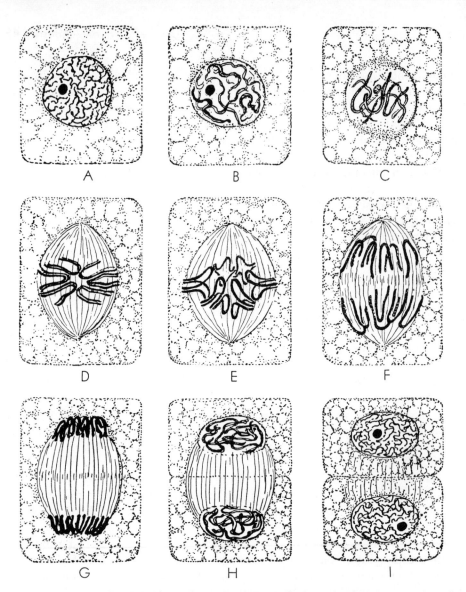

Fig. 27. The progress of mitosis, outlined in schematic form. As the cell prepares to divide, the chromosomes appear as distinct bodies in the nucleus, with a split along their length. The spindle appears at metaphase and separates the two chromatids of each chromosome at anaphase, after which the cell plate cuts the cell into two new cells.

halves called *chromatids*. The increasing visibility of the chromosomes is probably caused by a loss of water, which compacts its stainable parts more densely. Of equal importance, however, is the fact that the chromosomes become shorter and thicker by a process that transforms the slender chromatids into a coiled structure, much as a thin wire can be transformed into a coiled spring. As the chromatids continue to shorten throughout prophase, the coils will decrease in number as they are increasing in diameter.

During prophase, the nucleoli, which are formed by particular chromosomes, are initially prominent, but they diminish in size toward the end of the stage and disappear. The nuclear membrane also disintegrates in late prophase, contraction of the chromosomes ceases, and *metaphase* begins.

The disappearance of the nuclear membrane coincides with the appearance of a new structure in the cytoplasm, the *spindle*, which, chemically, consists of long-chain protein molecules oriented in a longitudinal

Fig. 28. Stages in mitosis. Top row: prophase, metaphase, and anaphase in the broad bean roottip; the gap in one arm of the longest two chromosomes represents the site where the nucleolus was attached, and can be seen at both metaphase and anaphase. (Courtesy of Dr. T. Merz.) Bottom row: metaphase, early anaphase, and telophase with cell plate forming, and late anaphase and prophase in the onion root. (Copyright by General Biological Supply House, Inc., Chicago.)

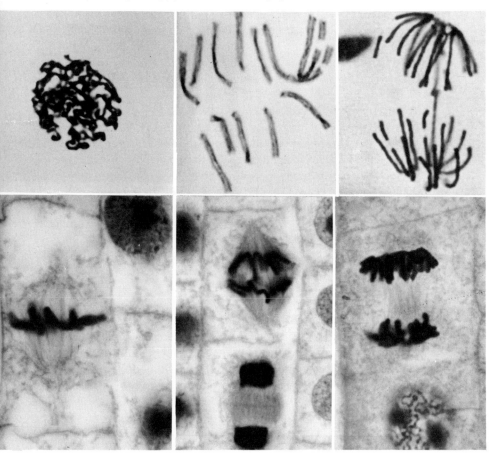

direction between two *poles*. Chemical analysis of the cell has indicated that approximately 15 per cent of the cytoplasmic proteins go into its make-up. Once the spindle is formed, the chromosomes move through the cytoplasm to it, and become fastened by their *centromeres* to a region midway between the poles called the *equator* of the spindle, a position of apparent equilibrium. The centromere of each chromosome always contacts the spindle at the equator; the arms of the chromosomes are not so restricted in position and are randomly oriented. It is relatively easy to prevent the spindle from forming by putting the cells in a solution of *colchicine,* an alkaloid drug. The chromosomes then lie free in the cell, and their morphology can be easily seen.

The centromere is the organ of movement. Without it, a chromosome cannot orient on the spindle, and the chromatids cannot separate from each other later. The position of the centromere is visible in the metaphase chromosome by a constriction which is formed, and since the position is characteristic for each chromosome, the centromere divides the chromosome into two arms of varying length. Very few chromosomes have strictly terminal centromeres.

Anaphase follows metaphase in the mitotic cycle. The centromeres now divide so that each chromatid has its own centromere; they then move apart from each other to initiate a slow movement that will take sister chromatids to opposite poles. Termination of anaphase movement occurs when the chromosomes form a densely packed group at the two poles.

At this point, anaphase ends and *telophase* begins. The events are essentially the reverse of those occurring in prophase: the nuclear membrane forms, the chromosomes uncoil to become slender threads again, and the nucleoli and chromocenters make their appearance. The nucleus as a whole takes on an interphase character. At the equator a new cell wall forms. Initially the *cell plate*, as it is called, is formed within the confines of the spindle, but soon it crosses to the outer walls to segment the cytoplasm into roughly equal parts. The spindle then disintegrates, mitosis is completed, and two new cells are formed.

Mitosis in Animal Cells

The cells of the whitefish (*Coregonus*) embryo illustrate very beautifully the mitotic process and reveal the differences that distinguish animal from plant mitosis (Fig. 29). The behavior of the chromosomes is the same in both forms though they are more numerous and smaller in the whitefish cell than in those of the onion or broad bean. The most immediate difference is in the process of spindle formation. As Fig. 29 reveals, the whitefish cell in prophase shows a radiating structure adjacent to the nuclear membrane. This is the *centrosome,* with astral *rays* radiating from it and with a central body or *centriole* contained within it. During prophase, or even before, the centriole divides in two, and the halves migrate along the membrane until they lie opposite each other. When the nuclear membrane breaks down, they organize the cellular proteins into the spindle in such a way that the centrioles are at the poles with the spindle between them. It is not known how the centrosomes and centrioles perform this task. Astral rays also extend into the cytoplasm, but they perform no known function unless they are included in the spindle.

Fig. 29. Stages in mitosis in the whitefish. (A) Prophase, with spindle beginning to form; (B) Metaphase; (C) Anaphase; (D) Telophase, with the furrow cutting the cell into two new daughter cells. (Copyright by General Biological Supply House, Inc., Chicago.)

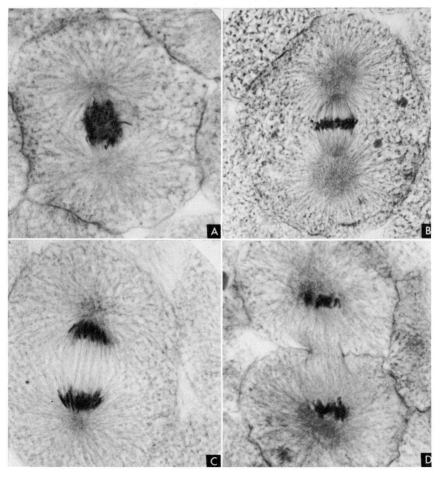

The division of the whitefish mother cell into two new daughter cells is another point of difference. A process of *furrowing*, beginning at the outer edges of the cell in the vicinity of the equator, cleaves the cell in two. Plant cells, with their rigid cell walls, cannot do this, and consequently they have evolved the cell plate formation to accomplish the same thing.

Other Aspects of Cell Division

Many aspects of cell division are not explained simply by a description of the mitotic process as it passes from one interphase through the various stages to the succeeding interphase. Yet even a descriptive analysis reveals that a completed mitotic cycle is a delicately balanced and coordinated affair, and that the nucleus, the cytoplasm, and their constituent parts come in on cue to play their appointed roles. One mistake and an abnormal cell results.

What is the significance of mitosis? It is, above all else, part of the process of growth. Although the dance of the chromosomes, the formation of the spindle, and the formation of daughter cells are the more obvious parts of the drama, it also involves the assimilation of materials from the outside, their transformation through breakdown and synthesis into new cellular parts, and the utilization of energy. Cell enlargement also takes place. We know of no cells, except the fertilized egg and a few of its derivative cells, that simply divide from one large cell into two others of half size and again into four cells of quarter size. This is not the way mitosis proceeds, for interspersed in the process are periods of growth; mitosis is a tumultuous affair, from which the cells must recover before proceeding again through the cycle.

Of great significance to growth, too, is the fact that mitosis insures a continuous succession of similarly endowed cells. Chaos would result if only a random array of cells of varying qualities and capacities were to reproduce themselves; organized growth must proceed from cells of similar nature that can subsequently be molded according to the demands of the species. The species could not otherwise persist. We mentioned earlier that the chromosome is an intricate fabric composed of nucleic acids and proteins. Since the nucleus is the control center of the cell, and since the nucleus contains little else but chromosomes, the chromosomes must be the regulators of cellular metabolism and the structural characteristics of the cell. Therefore, if two cells are to behave similarly they must have the same amount and type of nucleic acids and proteins. The longitudinal duplication of the chromosomes into identical chromatids and their segregation to the poles at anaphase must be exact to the minutest degree; mitosis provides the mechanism needed. When does duplication take place? If we probe the cell with radioactive isotopes, we find that the nucleic acids and the proteins of the chromosomes are formed during interphase, just prior to the onset of the division process. We know little about chromosomal duplication except the time of its occurrence, but there is no denying the wondrous fact that an exact lineal heredity is established both from cell to cell and from organism to organism. From the time a particular species was formed, this process of cell division has gone on with an exactitude that almost defies the imagination. Accidents and variations do occur, and indeed they must if evolution is to take place, but they are relatively few in number.

Let us ask another question. Why is it that cells divide? Or, in reverse, why is it that reproducing cells stop dividing? If we take a cell such as an amoeba, we can observe that it reaches a certain size and then divides. If we starve it, it will shrink and stop dividing. It would appear, therefore, that cell division is an attempt to keep a fairly constant ratio between the amount of the nucleus and the amount of the cytoplasm. This view makes sense, for if the nucleus governs the activities of the cell, it can exercise efficient control over only a certain amount of cytoplasmic material. If the cytoplasm should exceed a certain amount, the power of the nucleus over it becomes less and less. For example, an amoeba can be prevented from dividing by cutting off each day bits of the growing cytoplasm, thus keeping the ratio of cytoplasm to nucleus constant. However, the problem isn't quite so simple as it might appear. If the nucleus of an actively dividing amoeba is inserted into an amoeba that is in a quiescent state (this can be done with a micro-pipette without damaging either the nucleus or the cytoplasm), nothing happens unless both the nucleus and the cytoplasm are ready for cell division to occur. What we mean by a state of maturity is still somewhat uncertain, but obviously both these parts must be prepared for division before the process of mitosis can go on in any organized fashion.

Certainly a cell that is about to enter mitosis needs energy, which is largely obtained from the breakdown of carbohydrates, and any factor that increases the cell's consumption of energy-yielding food naturally tends to stimulate it into division. We can artificially feed cells in a culture, but we still are pretty much in the dark concerning what mechanism sets off the chain of events that leads to division. We do know, however, that the synthesis of new DNA and protein must precede cell division, indicating that the coordinated action of a good many enzymes is needed in addition to a sufficient supply of food.

How long does it take a cell to go through the entire process of division, and what is the time spent in each stage of mitosis? This can best be determined by examining a dividing cell (cells grown in tissue culture are good for this type of study) under the phase-contrast microscope while it is still alive. We find that the rate of cell division is characteristic of the organism in question, and that the rate can be governed very easily by varying such factors as nutrition and temperature. Let us take the human fibrocyte (a type of generalized connective cell) as an example, since it is now possible to grow these readily in tissue culture. The entire cycle of cell division takes approximately 18 hours from its initiation to its completion, that is, from interphase to interphase. Yet from the beginning of prophase to the end of telophase requires only about 45 minutes. The cell thus spends approximately 17 hours preparing itself for division, after which it goes through the process in a relatively explosive fashion. Other cells, and indeed other strains of fibrocytes, may take longer. To understand the process of cell division, therefore, it is quite clear that we must know what is taking place in the preparatory stages leading up to the initiation of prophase. As we have indicated, our knowledge of this is very limited at the present time.

Figure 30 shows the division cycle of the neuroblast cells of the grasshopper embryo. These are cells lying on the surface of the embryo which divide to form tissue that eventually becomes incorporated into the nervous system of the grasshopper at maturity. It can be seen that at 38°C the length of time for the entire process is approximately 3½ hours. A very large portion of the time, in fact about half of it, is spent in prophase. Metaphase and anaphase are fairly short, but the reorganization of the nucleus in telophase takes a longer period of time. Interphase in

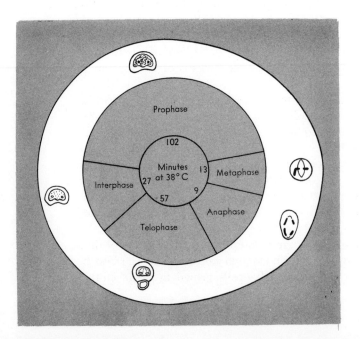

Fig. 30.   Time sequence of mitosis in certain cells of a grasshopper embryo that complete their cycle in 208 minutes at 38°C. At lower temperatures, the cycle would be correspondingly lengthened. (Redrawn from J. G. Carlson.)

this particular type of cell is quite short, compared to that of the human cell described above. If, however, the temperature is lowered to 26°C, the whole division cycle is lengthened to approximately 8 hours instead of 3½.

The effect of temperature on the rate of cell division is strikingly revealed in studies that have been made of the stamen hair cells of a plant called *Tradescantia*. The hairs are long filaments consisting of a chain of individual cells; only the terminal cell goes through division. A complete division takes place in about 135 minutes if the temperature is 10°C, but at 45°C it takes only 30 minutes. As you would expect, organisms vary greatly in their time of division. Bacteria, at 37°C, will go through a division every 15–20 minutes, while roottip cells generally take about 22 hours at room temperature. Some roottip cells continue to divide at 0°C, but we know little about the time span involved at that temperature. Warm-blooded animals show a lesser degree of tolerance; cell division ceases at temperatures below 24°C or above 46°C.

The continuation of any species, man or amoeba, oak tree or bacteria, depends on an unending succession of individuals. No organism is immortal, so its population must reproduce if it is to escape extinction. In unicellular organisms such as the amoeba, mitosis serves this function; it is a reproductive device that leads to the continued formation of new individuals. And, since mitosis is a mechanism that maintains the chromosome number in each amoeba constant, all offspring arising through mitosis have the same number of chromosomes as the original amoeba.

The amoeba, however, like many unicellular and some multicellular organisms, is asexual; it does not produce sexual cells—*eggs* and *sperm*. But other unicellular and most multicellular organisms reproduce by sexual means; sometime during their life cycle they produce *gametes* (a general term applied to any type of sexual cell) which unite in pairs to form a single new cell called a *zygote*. From this cell a new individual will develop. The union of gametes is called *fertilization* or *syngamy*.

In the alga, *Pandorina morum* (Fig. 16), the gametes are similar in appearance, and are produced by the simple transformation of any cell in the colony. These are *isogametes* (*iso* = like). When the gametes differ in size, as they do in most sexual organisms, they are known as *heterogametes* (*hetero* = unlike); the larger one is the egg and the smaller is the sperm.

54

It is important to recognize that when two gametes unite through fertilization, the principal event is the fusion of gametic nuclei. Let us consider what this means in terms of chromosome number. The cells of the human, for example, contain forty-six chromosomes. If we assume for the moment that mitosis is the only type of cell division, the human egg and sperm will each contain forty-six chromosomes, since they arise by mitosis from the original zygote. The zygote formed by their union would then contain 92 chromosomes, and so, too, will the eggs or sperm produced by the individual developing from the new zygote. The individuals of the next generation would possess 184 chromosomes, and by the end of the tenth generation each individual would have cells containing 23,332 chromosomes.

Very obviously, this is a ridiculous state of affairs. The illustration was used merely to emphasize the fact that, in a sexually breeding population, the increase in chromosome number resulting from fertilization cannot go on indefinitely. Sometime during the life cycle of an individual there must be a compensatory mechanism which reduces this number, for we know that the cells of individuals belonging to the same species have a very striking constancy of chromosome number. Thus, normal human cells have 46 chromosomes, those of maize have 20, the mouse 40, the rat 42, and so forth. The lowest number known is 2, found in a round worm, while some plants have numbers as high as several hundred. This constancy is repeated generation after generation. The gametes, therefore, must have half the number of chromosomes found in the zygote and in the other cells of the body (since the latter arise from the zygote by mitosis). The reduction in number of chromosomes is accomplished by a special type of cell division called *meiosis*, which in its barest essentials consists of *two nuclear divisions accompanied by but one division of the chromosomes.*

Before considering the details of meiosis, and the features which make this type of cell division different from that of mitosis, we will need to recognize certain terms that conveniently describe the various chromosomal states. The chromosomes in the nuclei of gametes are called the *reduced, gametic, haploid,* or *n* number, while those in the zygote and all cells derived from it by mitosis are termed the *unreduced, zygotic, diploid,* or *2n* number. Thus, the human egg, prior to fertilization, would possess 23 chromosomes in contrast to the 46 in the zygote. Furthermore, the 46 chromosomes are not individually different; they exist as 23 pairs of chromosomes, with the members of each pair being similar in shape, size, and genetic content to each other. The members of each pair are said to be *homologous* to each other, and *non-homologous* with respect to the other chromosomes. Every pair of homologous chromosomes, or *homologues,* thus consists of one member contributed by the sperm and one by the egg.

Meiosis is a rather complicated type of cell division, yet the remarkable thing about it is that, like mitosis, it is essentially the same wherever it is encountered. Consequently a single account of it applies equally well to a fungus, an insect, a flowering plant, or a man. Except for the type of cell resulting from meiosis, the process is similar in both sexes as well.

The Stages of Meiosis

Meiosis can be separated into a sequence of steps similar to those in mitosis (Figs. 31 and 32). Prophase, however, is longer in duration and profoundly modified, and five separate stages are recognizable.

The *leptotene* stage initiates meiosis. The meiotic cells and their nuclei are generally larger than those of the surrounding tissues. The chromosomes, present in the diploid number, are thinner and longer than in mitosis, and because of this are difficult to distinguish individually. Leptotene chromosomes, however, differ from those in ordinary mitotic

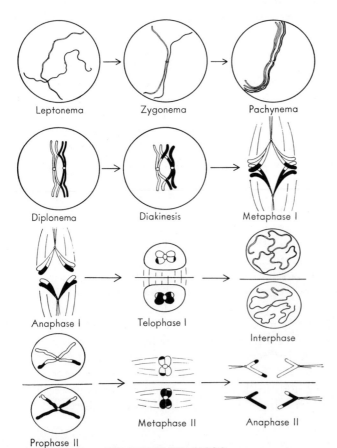

Leptonema   Zygonema   Pachynema

Diplonema   Diakinesis   Metaphase I

Anaphase I   Telophase I

Interphase

Fig. 31. Diagrammatic representation of the stages of division in meiosis I and II. For simplification, only one pair of homologues is included. (M. M. Rhoades, *Journal of Heredity*, 41, 1950, 59–67.)

Prophase II   Metaphase II   Anaphase II

THE STAGES OF MEIOSIS

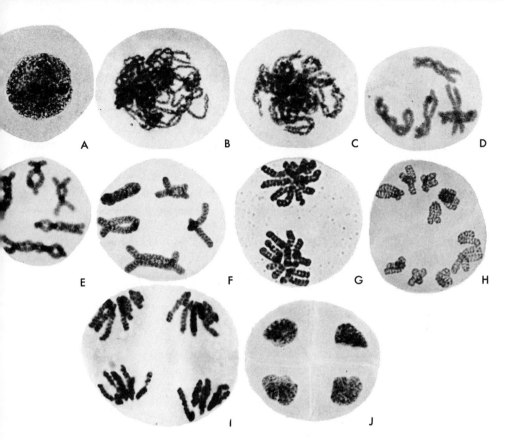

Fig. 32. Stages of meiosis in *Trillium*. (A) zygotene; (B) pachytene; (C) early diplotene; (D) late diplotene; (E) diakinesis; (F) metaphase I; (G) late anaphase I; (H) metaphase II (prophase II is absent in this plant); (I) anaphase II; (J) quartet stage, with four microspores. The development of the microspores to form the male gametophyte and the mature pollen grain is illustrated in Fig. 47. (Courtesy Dr. A. H. Sparrow.)

prophase in two ways: 1) they appear to be longitudinally single rather than double, and 2) their structure is more definite and a series of dense granules, or *chromomeres*, occurs at irregular intervals along their length. The chromomeres are characteristic in number, size, and position, and consequently can be used as landmarks to identify particular chromosomes. It has been estimated that in the garden lily, for example, there are about 2,000 chromomeres in the entire set of 24 chromosomes.

Movement of the chromosomes initiates the *zygotene* stage, and this movement appears to result from an attraction force that brings together homologous chromosomes. The pairing of homologues, known as *synapsis*, begins at one or more points along the length of the chromosomes and then proceeds, much as would a zipper, to unite the homologues along their entire length. This is an exact, not a random, process, for the chromomeres in one homologue synapse exactly with the corresponding ones in the other homologue (Fig. 33). When synapsis is complete, the nucleus will appear as if only the haploid number of chromosomes is present. Each, however, is a pair, and these are referred to as *bivalents*.

If the zygotene stage is thought of as the period of active synapsis, the next, or *pachytene*, stage is the stable period. The paired chromosomes of each bivalent are easily seen, and since the chromosomes have shortened and thickened, they are more readily distinguished one from the other. The chromomeres and the attachment of the nucleolus to a particular chromosome may be visible with high magnification (Fig. 34).

The pachytene stage ends abruptly when the synaptic forces of attraction lapse and the homologous chromosomes separate from each other. This is the *diplotene* stage, and as Fig. 34 indicates, each chromosome now consists of two chromatids. The bivalent, therefore, is composed of four chromatids. Longitudinal division of each chromosome, except in the region of the centromere, took place during the pachytene stage, but did not become obviously evident until the attraction between homologues ceased.

Separation of the homologues, however, is not complete. At one or more points along their length, contact is retained by means of *chiasmata* (singular, *chiasma*). Each chiasma results from an exchange of chromatids between the two homologues; we shall discuss later in this chapter the significance of this phenomenon as it relates to heredity.

When only one chiasma has formed, the bivalent in the diplotene stage appears as a cross (Fig. 34). If two are formed, the bivalent is generally ring-shaped; if three or more form, the homologues assume a looped appearance. In different cells, the number and approximate positions of the chiasmata vary, even for the same bivalent, but, as a rule, long

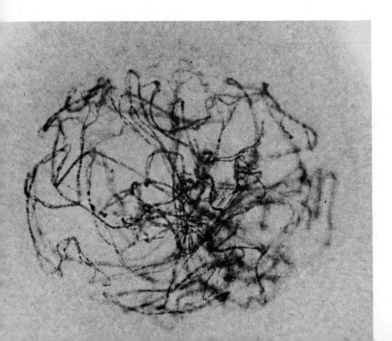

Fig. 33. Zygotene stage of meiosis in the regal lily, *Lilium regale*. In the left-hand lower corner, both paired and unpaired regions of the homologues are visible. (Courtesy of Dr. J. McLeish.)

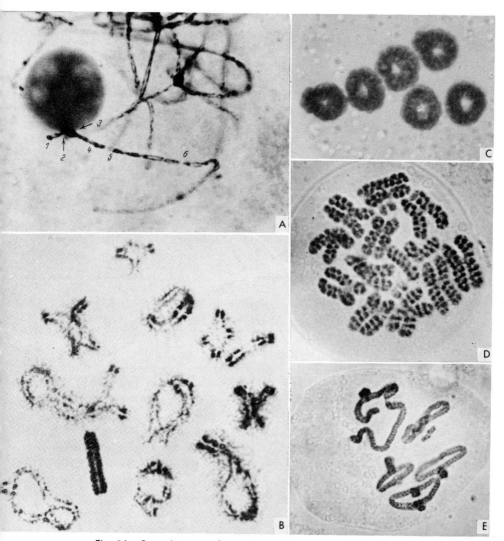

Fig. 34. Several stages of meiosis in different organisms. (A) Pachytene in maize, showing chromosome 6 and its attached nucleolus; the double nature of the chromosomes is evident, and the numbers indicate identifiable regions (B. McClintock, *Zeitschr. Zelif. u. Mikr. Anat.* 21: 294–328, 1934). (B) Diplotene stage in a spermatocyte of a grasshopper, *Schistocerca gregaria;* the unpaired X-chromosome is seen as a deeply stained rod, while chiasmata are visible in the paired homologues (J. H. Tjio and A. Levan, *Ana. Est. Exp. Aula Dei* 3, 2: 225–228, 1954). (C) Metaphase I in *Tradescantia,* with most of the chiasmata at terminal positions. (D) Flattened anaphase I, showing the coiled structure of the chromosomes in *Tradescantia.* (E) Metaphase I in *Tradescantia,* with the chiasmata at interstitial positions; compare with (C).

chromosomes have more chiasmata than short ones, although even the shortest seem to be able to form at least one.

The next prophase stage is called *diakinesis,* but the distinction between it and the diplotene stage is not a sharp one. However, during diakinesis the nucleolus becomes detached from its special bivalent and disappears, and the bivalents are considerably more contracted. Also, as contraction proceeds, the chiasmata tend to lose their original position and move towards the ends of the chromosomes.

Mention has been made of the fact that the chromosomes shorten as they progress from the leptotene stage onward through prophase. This is accomplished by the development of a series of coils, which gradually decrease in number as their diameters increase. The process is no different from that which shortens the chromosomes in mitosis; the coils, however, are more easily observed, particularly when the cells have been pre-treated with ammonia vapors or dilute cyanide solution before staining. Figure 34 illustrates the coils as they appear in the spiderwort, *Tradescantia*.

The breakdown of the nuclear membrane and the appearance of the spindle terminate prophase and initiate the *first metaphase of meiosis*. The bivalents then orient themselves on the spindle, but instead of all centromeres being on the equatorial plate, as happens in mitosis, each bivalent is located such that its two centromeres lie on either side of and equidistant from the plate. This appears to be a position of equilibrium.

The *first anaphase* of meiosis begins with the movement of the chromosomes to the poles. The two centromeres of each bivalent remain undivided, and their movement to the opposite poles of the spindle causes the remaining chiasmata to slip off and free the homologues from each other. When movement ceases, a reduced or haploid number of chromosomes will be located at each pole. Unlike mitotic anaphase, in which the chromosomes appear longitudinally single, each chromosome now consists of two distinctly separated chromatids united only at their centromeres.

The nucleus then forms, the chromosomes uncoil, and the meiotic cell is divided in two by a wall or membrane. This period is the *first telophase of meiosis*.

After an interphase which, depending on the species involved, may be short, long, or even absent altogether, the chromosomes in each of the two haploid cells enter the *second meiotic division*. If an interphase is absent, the chromosomes pass directly from the first telophase to the *second prophase* without any change in appearance. If an interphase is present, a nuclear membrane forms in telophase, the chromosomes uncoil, and a somewhat more prolonged second prophase is found. But, whatever the case, the chromosomes reaching the *second metaphase* are essentially unchanged from what they were in the previous anaphase; i.e., *no chromosomal reproduction occurred during interphase*, and the centromere of each chromosome remains undivided. A spindle forms in each of the two cells, and, at the *second anaphase*, the centromeres divide and the chromosomes move to the poles. The nuclei are reorganized during the *second telophase,* giving four haploid nuclei which become segregated into individual cells by segmentation of the cytoplasm.

Looking back over the events of meiosis, we find that the chromosomes remained unchanged in longitudinal structure from the diplotene stage to the end of the second meiotic division. The reproduction of each chromosome occurred during pachytene, but this was followed by two divisions, the first separating the homologues from each other to reduce chromosome number, an event made possible because synapsis brought them together, and the second separating the two chromatids of each chromosome.

At this point you may well ask why the reduction in chromosome number could not be accomplished just as efficiently with a single division instead of two. No logical answer can be given, but where only a single meiotic division is found, as happens during sperm formation in the normally haploid male honey bee, it is essentially like the second rather than the first division. In organisms that have a diploid chromosome number, the two divisions make more sense, particularly when considered from the point of view of heredity.

Genetic Significance of Meiosis

We have presented meiosis as a logical and necessary part of the life cycle of a sexually reproducing organism, i.e., it is the opposite of fertilization as regards the number of chromosomes. So far as heredity is concerned, two additional implications need clarification.

Figure 35 illustrates the segregation of chromosomes, with the paternal chromosomes indicated in black, the maternal ones in white. Each bivalent at the first meiotic metaphase would, of course, consist of two homologues, one from each parent. The orientation of this and other bivalents on the spindle is entirely at random, so that segregation at anaphase leads to a random distribution of chromosomes. The haploid cells resulting would therefore contain a mixture of paternal and maternal chromosomes. When 4 pairs of chromosomes are involved, 16 different combinations of 4 are possible. The number possible can be readily determined by calculating the value of 2^n, when n equals the number of pairs of chromosomes. In man, who has 23 pairs, the number of possible gametic chromosome combinations is 2^{23}, or 8,388,608. The chances of any single sperm or egg containing only paternal or maternal chromosmes is, therefore, negligible.

The distribution of paternal and maternal chromatin to their offspring through gametes is further complicated by the process of chiasma

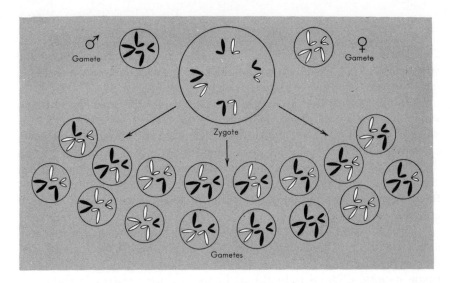

Fig. 35. Diagram to represent the random segregation of paternal (black) and maternal (white) chromosomes during meiosis. Crossing over and linkage are not indicated.

formation. As we pointed out before, a chiasma results from an exchange between chromatids in the two homologues. One of these is from a maternal chromosome, the other from a paternal chromosome. If we further consider that the chromosome consists of a number of genes strung along its length, and that the genes in one homologue may be slightly different from those in the other as the result of mutations, a situation such as that illustrated in Fig. 36 can be envisaged.

The genes in the paternal (black) chromosome are designated by capital letters from *A* to *E*, those in the maternal (white) one from *a* to *e*.

Fig. 36. The genetical consequences of crossing over. (A) A bivalent, consisting of a paternal (black) and a maternal (white) homologue, has formed, and crossing over has taken place between genes A and B, and C and D. (B) At anaphase the two chromatids in each segregating chromosome are no longer alike genetically. (C) The chromatids are now separated and two of them have a different genetic composition, while the other two remain as before.

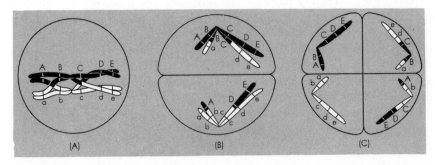

It should be remembered, however, that any single chromosome may have hundreds of different genes along its length. Chiasmata have formed as the result of exchanges between A and B, and between C and D. (In genetical terminology, an exchange of chromatids is called *crossing over,* and the genes A to E and a to e would constitute *linkage groups.*) The actual mechanism responsible for chiasma formation is not known for certain, but it seems clear that it occurs just prior to the diplotene stage when the chromosomes undergo transformation from a longitudinally single to a double structure. The important thing, however, is that chiasma formation breaks up linkage groups, and therefore alters the set of genes which the chromosome possessed before entering meiosis. The chromatids eventually are distributed to the four haploid cells, and it is clear that each gamete is genetically different from the others.

We see, therefore, that both the random segregation of paternal and maternal chromosomes and the breaking up of linkage groups through chiasma formation insure that the haploid cells resulting from meiosis will have a variable combination of genes. Since these cells contribute through fertilization to the next generation, the individuals of that generation must exhibit a comparable genetic variation. It is this inherited variability which natural selection acts upon to bring about the evolution of organisms. Sexual reproduction, with its complementary phenomena of fertilization and meiosis, is a means not only for the production of new individuals, but of new individuals *that vary among themselves.* In this sense meiosis differs greatly from mitosis, which, in its production of similarly endowed cells, is a conservative process of reproduction.

6

The Cell

in

Reproduction—

Animals

Reproduction is generally defined as the process by which a plant or animal gives rise to one of its own kind. We have, of course, already discussed some reproductive processes: chromosome duplication, cell division, and multiplication of such structures as plastids and mitochondria. All of these are duplicative processes, but we shall restrict our discussion here to the structure and behavior of cells which contribute to the formation of new individuals.

Asexual Reproduction

When an organism such as an amoeba divides by mitosis to form two progeny, obviously only one parent is involved. This is *uniparental* or *asexual* reproduction. In the amoeba, it is the only form of reproduction, although in other single-celled organisms it may alternate with sexual reproduction. In multicellular forms, mitosis only increases the number of cells, but other sorts of asexual reproduction are found. One of these is *budding*, a process by which small bits of the organism pinch off, free themselves from the parent, and then develop into organisms similar to the parent. This occurs in the familiar laboratory animal, *Hydra*, as well as in many jellyfishes and corals. Other animals, such as the flatworms, earthworms, and starfishes, can form new individuals from broken-off segments, and in at least one type of flat-

64

worm the parent regularly undergoes spontaneous *fragmentation,* with each fragment developing into a new individual. In some cases of asexual reproduction, therefore, the parent survives while in others parental identity is lost among the offspring.

Sexual Reproduction

When two parents or cells are involved and each offspring results from the union of cells from each parent, the process is *sexual reproduction.* The parents may be so similar in appearance, as in *Paramecium,* that it is impossible to distinguish males from females; or the parents may be *bisexual* or *hermaphroditic,* as in the earthworm or oyster, and may be capable of producing both eggs and sperm, although not necessarily capable of self-fertilization; or, as is more usual, the parents may be readily separated into males and females, with each producing its own kind of reproductive cell, or gamete, in special organs developed for this purpose. These are the *gonads,* which include the *ovaries* in females and the *testes* in males.

These cells form the *germ line,* a continuous chain of cells which are set aside early in embryonic development, which are preserved from those forces causing differentiation in other cells of the body, and which span the gap between sexual generations. Meiosis and fertilization are, of course, key processes in a sexual life cycle, but developmental processes are also involved and it is with them that we shall concern ourselves here, using the mammalian cycle as an example.

It is now well established that the development of the mammalian gonad and its germ cells is initiated by cells which migrate by amoeboid movement from other parts of the embryo into the gonadal region, or *genital ridge* (in the chicken, the circulatory system carries them). If cell migration is stopped, no gonad is formed, but if the cells arrive at the genital ridge area, they cause neighboring cells to enclose them. This is the beginning of the gonad. The migratory germ cells or their mitotic derivatives are believed to be those which eventually form the gametes; the enclosing cells and their derivatives would then form the remainder of the gonadal tissue. If the gonad is to become a testis, a *germinal epithelium* is formed, and cells from this tissue develop into chord-like twisted masses known as *semeniferous tubules,* which will produce sperm. If the gonad is to become an ovary, the migrating cells also form a germinal epithelium and increase in number, but as they mature they sink into surrounding tissue and develop into *ovarian follicles* that contain eggs or *ova.*

The Egg

Figure 37 is a section of a mammalian ovary. On the outside is the germinal epithelium which gives rise to the *oogonial cells*. These develop early in life and do not increase in numbers after sexual maturity. Initially, the *primary oocytes* lie close to the germinal epithelium, but later they increase in size and sink into the interior of the ovary where they become surrounded by the *follicle cells*, which probably have both a protective and a nutritive function. The whole structure is known as a *Graafian follicle*. During this process of enlargement and encapsulation, the oocyte is building up reserve food material, the yolk. This may be protein or fatty in nature, and in mammals it is generally distributed throughout the cytoplasm as yolk spheres or granules. In the frog, however, the yolk so completely fills the cell that the cytoplasm is restricted to a small fraction of the cell surrounding the nucleus; the well-known yolk in the hen's egg is also enormous compared to the amount of cytoplasm.

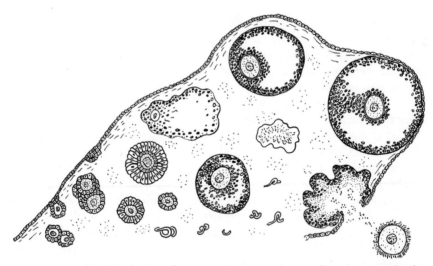

Fig. 37. Section of a mammalian ovary, showing the progressive development of the oocytes as they arise from the germinal epithelium, increase in size, sink into the interior of the ovary wall, and finally escape to the outside by rupture of the wall of the Graafian follicle.

Eventually, the Graafian follicle ruptures and the egg or ovum is released from the ovary. By this time, however, meiosis has been initiated. Only a *single* functional cell results, however. The other three cells, or *polar bodies*, are cast off and will degenerate, *but the process has effectively reduced the chromosome number without depriving the egg of the cytoplasm and yolk the embryo will need when it begins to develop.*

The first meiotic division in the primary oocyte takes place close to the cell membrane, and the outermost nucleus, together with a small amount of cytoplasm, is pinched off as a polar body (Fig. 38). The second meiotic division results in the pinching off of a second polar body; the first polar body, meanwhile, has also undergone a second meiotic division, thus giving a total of three polar bodies. The haploid nucleus remaining in the egg is now known as the *female pronucleus.* It sinks into the center of the cytoplasm and is ready for union with a similar haploid nucleus brought in by the sperm during fertilization.

The Sperm

The sperm are produced in the *semeniferous tubules* of the testes; these convoluted tubes make up 90 per cent of the male gonadal tissue. Each tube is lined with germinal *epithelium* and *Sertoli* cells (Fig. 39); the former give rise to the germ cells, while the latter, called "sperm mother cells," are thought to assist the newly formed sperm to undergo a ripening process while the sperm are in contact with them.

The germinal epithelium contains *spermatogonia,* cells which continue to increase their number by mitotic division until senility sets in. These mature into *primary spermatocytes,* which undergo a first meiotic division to produce *secondary spermatocytes;* the latter pass through a second meiotic division, giving four cells called *spermatids.* These be-

Fig. 38. Polar body formation in the egg of the whitefish, Coregonus. (A) Anaphase of the first meiotic division, with the first polar body being pinched off. (B) Metaphase of the second meiotic division, which will lead to the pinching off of a second polar body. In the meantime, the first polar body may also divide to give a total of three. (Copyright by General Biological Supply House, Inc., Chicago.)

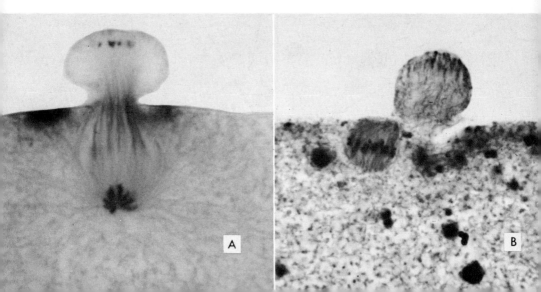

A   B

come motile sperm by a remarkable transformation of the entire cell.

The mature sperm consists essentially of a head and a tail. The head is a very much-compacted nucleus, capped by a structure known as the *acrosome*. It is derived from the Golgi materials of the spermatid, and apparently functions as a device for penetrating the egg during fertilization. Just back of the compacted nucleus is the *middle piece,* formed by an aggregation of the mitochondria. It develops as a sheath around the *filament,* or tail, and provides the tail with energy for locomotion. The filament, in turn, has developed as the result of a tremendous elongation of one of the centrioles; the other centriole remains just beneath the nucleus, and at the time of fertilization enters the egg along with the male nucleus. Virtually no cytoplasm except particulate structures is used to form the mature sperm.

Each spermatid, therefore, has been transformed from a rather undifferentiated cell into a highly specialized cell capable of reaching the egg under its own power, and of penetrating it once it has made contact.

Fertilization

The mature egg and sperm must unite with each other within a limited period of time, for neither has an indefinite life span. The critical

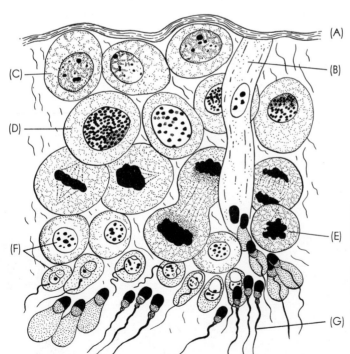

Fig. 39. Arrangements of cells and the order of progression of spermatogenesis in the semeniferous tubule: (A) basement membrane; (B) Sertoli cells; (C) spermatogonial cells, which by mitosis give rise to the primary spermatocytes (D); (E) secondary spermatocytes; (F) spermatids; (G) mature sperm.

time period may be a few minutes, or it may be spread over several hours or days. In mammals, fertilization occurs as the egg leaves the ovary and passes down the *oviduct* on its way to the *uterus*. Insects, however, mate only once, and sperm are stored in the female and used throughout the entire egg-laying period; in the honey bee, for example, this period may last a year or more. It is now possible to store mammalian sperm for an indefinite period by freezing them, and by means of *artificial insemination* the sperm of a single sire may be used to fertilize the eggs of many females; this practice has been widely used in animal breeding programs, thus passing on the superior hereditary qualities of one sire to many off-spring.

The essential process of fertilization is the union of male and female pronuclei, but the sperm also acts as an activating agent. That is, nature has insured against the egg beginning embryonic development alone; if it did, haploid embryos would result and life cycles would be hopelessly complicated. Unfertilized eggs of mammals and other related vertebrates can be induced to initiate development by various artificial means, but this rarely occurs naturally.

Fertilization is also a specific process in that the sperm of one species will not, as a rule, fertilize the egg of another species. It now appears that several chemicals are present to insure proper fertilization and to prevent the penetration of foreign sperm. The egg produces a protein substance called *fertilizin* which reacts with an *anti-fertilizin* on the surface of the sperm; fertilizin may act to attract sperm of its own kind, but once the two substances interact, the sperm becomes firmly attached to the egg membrane, and is then drawn into the interior of the egg. Other sperm are barred from entry by the changes that take place in the *vitelline membrane* of the egg, an outer coating found on most eggs.

Only the nucleus and one centriole of the sperm enter the egg. The former fuses with the female pronucleus, the latter divides and begins formation of the first division spindle. In summary, therefore, the entry of the sperm into an egg contributes (1) a stimulus to development, (2) a set of haploid chromosomes, which is the paternal hereditary contribution to the newly formed zygote, and (3) a centriole, which is involved in the machinery of cell division.

Parthenogenesis

The development of an egg without fertilization is called *parthenogenesis*. It occurs naturally in some groups of animals, and it can be induced in others where fertilization is a rule. In insects of the order Hymenoptera, which includes the bees and wasps, a fertilized egg develops

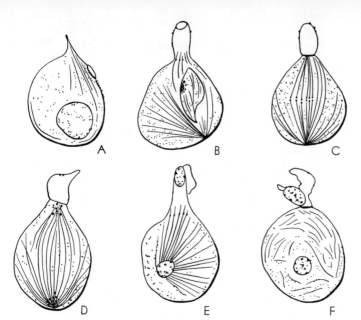

Fig. 40. Meiosis in the haploid male honeybee. The first meiotic division merely cuts off a small segment of cytoplasm containing no chromosomes (A and B), while the second division, which is essentially mitotic in character, cuts off a small nucleated cell which disintegrates; (C) metaphase II; (D) anaphase II; (E and F) terminal meiotic stages. (Redrawn from E. B. Wison, *The Cell in Development and Heredity*, 3rd ed., New York: Macmillan, 1925.)

into a female, while an unfertilized one develops parthenogenetically into a male. The females, consequently, have a diploid number of chromosomes in each cell, and during egg formation, meiosis proceeds normally. The males, however, are haploid, but nevertheless the germ cells undergo meiosis and give rise to normal haploid sperm. This is accomplished (Fig. 40) by an abnormal first meiotic division. The chromosome number is not reduced, although a division of the cytoplasm occurs; the second division is mitotic-like and two nuclei are formed. Only one nucleus remains functional, however, so that one sperm instead of four is produced by each spermatocyte. Parthenogenesis imposes certain restrictions, therefore, on the regular life cycle of an organism, and that described above is only one example of many, but as you become acquainted with the great variety of life cycles you will find that meiosis is a flexible process capable of wide modifications. In each instance, however, any modification or absence of fertilization must be compensated for by an equivalent modification or absence of meiosis, for the two processes cannot be out of gear with each other if the species is to continue.

7

The Cell in Reproduction— Plants

In our discussion of sexual reproduction in animals, we stated that the animal body has a diploid character. Since only the gametes, arising through meiosis, are haploid, meiosis is part of the process of *gametogenesis*. In females this would be *oogenesis,* in males *spermatogenesis*.

If we turn to the plant kingdom, we can find a similar situation in a plant familiar to most of us. This is *Fucus*, the common brown alga, or rockweed, that grows along our rocky coasts and is exposed at low tides. Figure 41 illustrates the life cycle of *Fucus*. The body of the plant, like that of an animal, is diploid, since it developed from the fertilized egg. The sex organs are found in the inflated bladder-like tips of branches and are known as *oogonia* and *antheridia*. Oogonia are large cells whose contents divide, first by meiosis and then by mitosis, to produce eight eggs; antheridia are smaller cells that give rise in a similar manner to a large number of motile sperm. The gametes are released into the open sea, where fertilization takes place and where the zygote settles to the bottom and develops into a new plant. As in an animal, the gametes represent the only haploid portion of the life cycle.

Let us now contrast the life cycle of *Fucus* with that of *Gonium*, a small, green, sixteen-celled alga very similar to *Pandorina morum,* which was depicted in Fig. 16. As we pointed out on p. 24, the number of sixteen-celled colonies increases by mitosis, and each cell in the colony is able to form a new colony. The

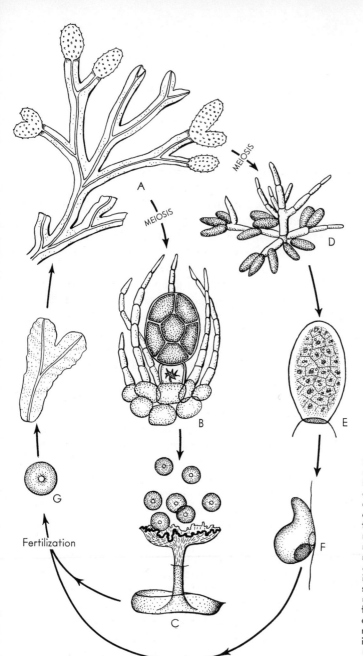

Fig. 41. Life cycle in the rockweed, *Fucus*. The diploid sporophyte (A) produces sexual organs in concavities in the inflated tips of the branches. Meiosis takes place in the oögonium (B), and eight nonmotile eggs (C) result; meiosis also occurs in the antheridia (D and E), giving rise to many motile sperm (F). The gametes unite during fertilization to form the zygote (G); this develops into a young sporophyte (H) and eventually into a mature sporophyte (A).

gametes, which are not distinguishable into male and female, arise by the simple transformation of a vegetative, colonial cell into a free, motile gamete. The gametes unite in pairs, but the resulting zygote does not form a new colony directly; instead, it passes through two meiotic divisions to form a four-celled colony, each cell of which is then capable of producing a sixteen-celled colony. Two striking differences, therefore, distinguish the life cycle of *Gonium* from that of animals or *Fucus*. In the first place, meiosis does not produce gametes, but rather vegetative cells; it is, therefore, not a part of the process of gametogenesis. Secondly, the body of the plant, i.e., the sixteen-celled colony, is haploid, not diploid.

We find, therefore, that haploid cells, as in *Gonium*, and diploid zygotes, as in *Fucus*, are both capable of developing into multicellular plant bodies. We may well ask, then: "Are there species in which both events take place?" The answer is emphatically in the affirmative, and the green sea lettuce, *Ulva*, is an example.

Ulva is an alga found attached to rocks at low tide. Its thin leaf-like body is only two cells in thickness. All of the plants look alike to the naked eye, but a microscopical examination would reveal the existence of two different kinds (Fig. 42). One of these is diploid, and any cell may undergo meiosis to produce four, and then eight, haploid motile zoospores. Each of these settles down eventually, loses its motility, and divides mitotically to form another plant. In this instance, however, the plant is haploid, not diploid, and any of its cells can, at maturity, be transformed into a free-swimming motile gamete. The gametes unite in pairs, and the zygote develops into a diploid plant to complete the life cycle.

These facts introduce us to a new concept, the *alternation of generations*. The complete life cycle of *Ulva* includes both a haploid and a diploid generation; these are independent of each other and each pro-

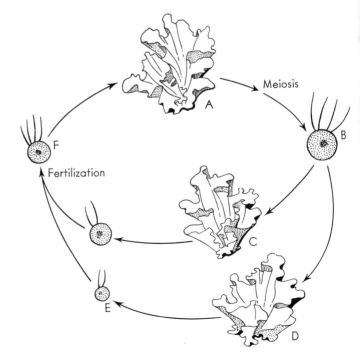

Fig. 42. Life cycle in the sea lettuce, *Ulva*. Each cell of the diploid sporophyte (A) is capable of producing 16 to 32 zoospores (B), with meiosis occurring during the first two divisions. The zoospores develop into haploid gametophytes (C and D), each cell of which produces a number of gametes (E); gametes from different plants unite in fertilization to produce a zygote (F) which develops into the sporophyte. Some species of *Ulva* are isogamous, some heterogamous; only in the latter could we distinguish male and female gametophytes.

duces its own kind of reproductive cell. The primitiveness of the life cycle is suggested by the fact that no special organs are needed to produce either zoospores or gametes. In fact, these two types of cell are very similar in appearance, but zoospores develop directly into a plant body while gametes fuse with each other first.

We meet two useful terms at this point. The haploid plant of *Ulva* is the *gametophyte* (gamete plant), representing the *sexual* part of the life cycle; the diploid plant, producing spores, is the *sporophyte* (spore plant), or the *asexual* phase. If we apply these terms to the life cycle of *Gonium*, we must then refer to the sixteen-celled colony as the gametophyte, and gametogenesis, as in *Ulva*, includes only the transformation of a vegetative cell into a gamete. The sporophytic, diploid generation in *Gonium* is represented only by the diploid zygote, and meiosis gives rise to a four-celled, haploid vegetative colony. The opposite is true in *Fucus*. The gametophytic generation is missing, with the gametes being the only haploid cells. The plant body is the sporophyte, but the situation is complicated because meiosis gives rise to gametes rather than to spores. There is no asexual generation, and *Fucus* consequently has a life cycle comparable to that in most higher animals. The *Fucus*-type of life cycle is rather unusual in plants, however, while the alternation of generations exhibited by *Ulva* is characteristic of the great majority of higher plants, although, as we shall see, the two generations need not be independent of each other. The *Gonium*-type of life cycle is typical of certain fungi and many algae.

In summary, therefore, we have learned that either the sporophyte or the gametophyte may dominate the life cycle, or, as in *Ulva*, that both may lead an independent existence. Secondly, meiosis is generally associated in plants with sporogenesis, only rarely with gametogenesis, and, lastly, the motility of the gametes reflects a dependence on an aquatic environment.

The seed-bearing plants, however, are dry-land inhabitants. They include the flowering plants (Angiosperms) and the conifers (Gymnosperms), and in order for reproduction to be carried on successfully in the absence of water, their reproductive organs and cells must undergo certain modifications. The ferns are of interest in this respect because they represent a transition between an existence that is wholly aquatic and one that is essentially non-aquatic (we recognize that water in the soil is necessary for life, but not directly necessary for reproduction).

Reproduction in the Ferns

The fern plant with which we are all familiar is the sporophytic part of the life cycle (Fig. 43). Although it has a root system, the leaves, or *fronds,* are its most conspicuous elements. During its reproductive stage, structures called *sporangia* are formed on the undersides of the fronds. Each sporangium contains within itself a group of diploid cells,

Fig. 43. Life cycle in the fern. (A) Diploid sporophyte which produces sporangia (B) on the undersides of the leaves. Meiosis reduces the chromosome number and produces the haploid asexual spores (C) which germinate to form the prothallus (D). Beneath the prothallus are the sexual organs, the antheridia (E) and archegonia (F), which give rise, respectively, to the sperm (G) and eggs (H). These unite in fertilization to form the diploid zygote (I) which, inside the archegonium, develops into the young sporophyte (J).

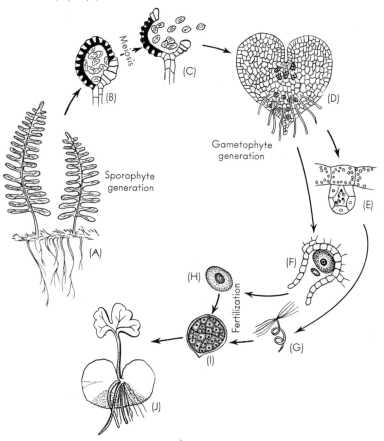

each one of which will undergo meiosis to form four haploid spores. When the sporangium is mature, it breaks open and the spores are released. If they fall on moist, shady soil, they germinate to produce a thin, somewhat heart-shaped structure called a *prothallus*. This is the gametophyte. Its cells contain chlorophyll for the manufacture of food, and it is attached to the soil by root-like hairs which can absorb water. As it reaches maturity, a group of sex organs are formed. Those near the base of the notch are the *archegonia* containing the eggs; those nearer the outer edge are the *antheridia* containing the sperm. The flagellated sperm must swim from the antheridia to the archegonia, and pass down the neck in order to effect fertilization. The germination of the spores, the existence of the delicate prothallus, and the act of fertilization are all dependent on an ample supply of water, and this need is a reflection of the fact that the ferns have not entirely escaped from their aquatic ancestry. Even though we frequently see ferns growing in what appears to be a dry habitat, water is vitally necessary during part of their life cycle.

The fertilized egg soon undergoes a series of mitoses, and a new sporophyte begins to develop (Fig. 43). A root is sent down, a young frond appears, and the gametophyte, having served its function, quickly withers and dies. The sporophyte may live indefinitely for many years, but the gametophyte has a very short life span.

Reproduction in the Flowering Plants

The flowering plants, or angiosperms, include the plants that most of us know best. They also represent the highest evolutionary development in the plant kingdom. In them, the reproductive trends exhibited by the ferns have been continued and extended until all dependence on an aquatic existence has been lost and adaptation to a dry-land environment has been completed. All evidences of gametic motility, consequently, have disappeared, and to compensate for this loss other devices have been developed for sexual reproduction. These are grouped together in the flower, and it takes only a glance to realize that the flower is a varied and wonderfully organized structure. But the sperm must still reach the egg to effect fertilization, and the wind or an insect replaces water as the agent of transportation. In general, colored flowers are insect-pollinated (the male cells are the *pollen grains*), while greenish ones, such as are found in the grasses, oaks, and willows, are wind-pollinated.

The simplicity of the lily flower makes it an ideal subject for examining the reproductive organs and cells. The lily plant, like the familiar fern, is the sporophyte, and the flower is a part of it. Its colored petals serve to attract insects, but the essential reproductive parts are the *pistil* (female) and *anthers* (male). Let us examine each in detail.

The pistil consists of three parts: the *ovary* which contains the female reproductive cells, the long *style,* and the *stigma* at its apex. The seeds will be formed in the ovary; one of the young seeds, or *ovules,* is enlarged to reveal the seed coats, and the single cell that is undergoing considerable enlargement (Fig. 44). This cell is known as the *megasporocyte*; it will undergo two meiotic divisions (stages I–III) to form four haploid nuclei (Fig. 45). No cross walls develop, but instead three of the nuclei fuse, to give a large cell containing two nuclei (stage IV). One *nucleus,* then, possesses three sets of chromosomes and is *triploid,* the other contains only one set and is haploid. Two successive mitotic divisions (stages V and VI) lead to a cell that contains eight nuclei, four of which are triploid and four haploid. Three of the triploid nuclei move to one end of the cell (which is now very much enlarged and called an *embryo sac*) and form a group whose function is probably nutritive. Walls

Fig. 44. Stages in the development of the megasporocyte in the lily. (A) Prophase in the first meiotic division (comparable to Fig. 45, Stage I); (B) comparable to Stage II; (C) comparable to Stage V—the upper nuclei are triploid, the lower two are haploid. (Copyright by General Biological Supply House, Inc., Chicago.)

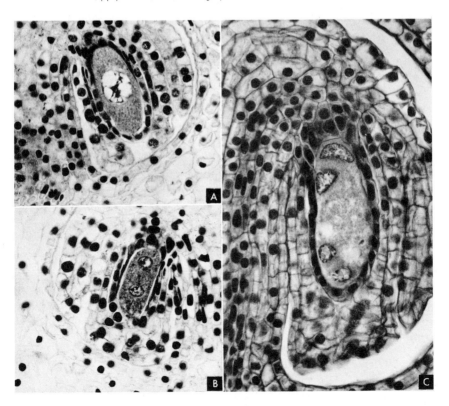

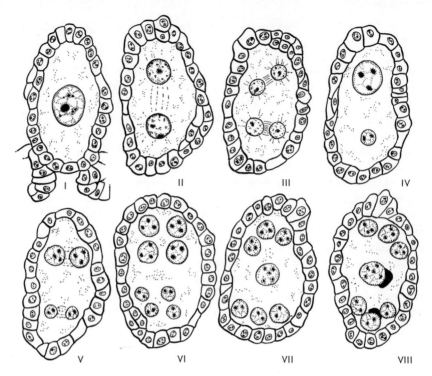

Fig. 45. Stages in the development of the megasporocyte into the embryo sac in the lily. Stage I, an enlarged megasporocyte prepares for meiotic divisions; Stages II and III, results of first and second meiotic divisions; Stage IV, fusion of three haploid nuclei gives a two-nucleate embryo sac with one nucleus being triploid, the other remaining haploid; Stages V and VI, two successive mitotic divisions give an embryo sac with four triploid nuclei and four haploid nuclei; Stage VII, rearrangement of the nuclei places three triploid nuclei at the upper end of the embryo sac and three haploid nuclei at the opposite end (the middle one is the egg), and a central fusion nucleus results from the union of a triploid and a haploid nucleus; Stage VIII, double fertilization, in which one sperm (dark area) unites with the egg to produce the zygote, and the other sperm unites with the fusion nucleus. The zygote will eventually form the embryo plant and the other nucleus will develop into the endosperm.

may form around them. Three of the haploid nuclei go to the micropylar end of the embryo sac; the one in the center is the egg, but the role òf the remaining two is unknown. The two nuclei that are left, one triploid and one haploid, join in the center of the embryo sac into the *fusion* nucleus, which now is *tetraploid* in character since it contains four sets of chromosomes.

The embryo sac is now ready for fertilization, but before considering the development of the male reproductive cells, we should point out that *the embryo sac is the female gametophyte* of the lily. Compare this with the prothallus of the fern, which is also a gametophyte. The embryo sac has no independent existence, it is actually parasitic on the sporophyte, and it is reduced to eight nuclei of which one is the egg.

The developing anther contains a number of cells that are destined to become the *pollen mother cells* or *microsporocytes*. These are indicated in Fig. 32, and at the end of meiosis four haploid cells, called *microspores*, will form from each one. These will develop into mature pollen grains. First, a single mitotic division produces a binucleate cell (Fig. 46), with one of the nuclei becoming the *tube nucleus*, and the other the *generative nucleus*, which will divide again, either in the same cell or in the *pollen tube*, to produce two sperm cells. A thick wall develops around the cell, and the mature pollen grain is ready to be released from the anther.

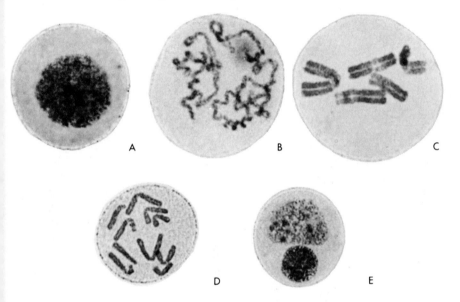

A   B   C

D   E

Fig. 46. Division of the microspore in *Trillium* to form the binucleate pollen grain. (A) interphase; (B) prophase; (C) metaphase; (D) anaphase; (E) mature pollen grain with the tube nucleus above and the generative nucleus below. The latter will divide in the pollen tube to form two sperm cells. This division should be viewed as a continuation of the development of one of the cells in Fig. 32 to form the male gametophyte. (Courtesy of Dr. A. H. Sparrow.)

The pollen grain is the male gametophyte. Like the embryo sac, it is parasitic within the sporophyte and is reduced to a single cell containing three nuclei: the tube nucleus and the two sperm. Wind or insects carry the pollen grains to the stigma where they germinate. A pollen tube is formed and grows down the style, eventually reaching the *micropyle* of the ovule. It forces its way to the embryo sac and discharges *both* sperm into it. One of these fuses with the egg to form the zygote, and the other joins with the fusion nucleus to form the *endosperm nucleus*.

This behavior leads us to characterize fertilization in the flowering plants as *double fertilization*. There is no counterpart of this phenomenon in the animal kingdom or in other lower plants.

The zygote soon undergoes mitosis and the resulting cells develop into an embryo sporophyte (Fig. 47). By this time, the endosperm nucleus has also begun to divide, and it will provide a mass of nutritive

Fig. 47. Two stages in the development of the embryo of shepherd's purse, *Capsella*. (A) Early stage, with the large basal cell at the bottom, the stalk cells in the middle, the embryo proper above, and all surrounded by the ovule wall. (B) More advanced stage of formation, with the basal and stalk cells below and the embryo proper above (note that two seed leaves of the embryo are forming). The cellular nature of the endosperm is evident in the cavity of the greatly enlarged embryo sac. (Copyright by General Biological Supply House, Inc., Chicago.)

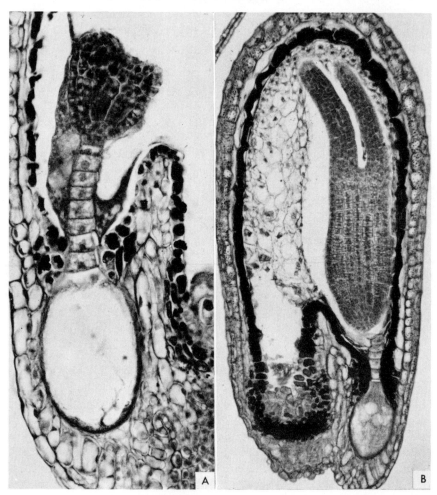

tissue upon which the developing sporophyte, or seedling, can feed. In starchy seeds such as the acorn, corn, and wheat, the endosperm makes up the greater part of the bulk, but in many smaller seeds the endosporm has been absorbed by the embryo by the time the seed has matured.

Upon examining a mature seed, therefore, we find that it is a mosaic composed of tissues of different origin. The seed coats are sporophytic tissue derived from the mother plant; the embryo is new sporophytic tissue derived from the zygote, and containing both paternal and maternal chromosomes; the endosperm is a new tissue we have not encountered previously, and it obviously has a different chromosomal composition and a different function. The seed, as such, is an adaptation to a dry-land existence, for it provides a means of keeping the young embryo in a dormant condition until conditions are appropriate for germination. Without the seed as a means of reproduction, and without the adaptation and reduction of the gametophyte, the flowering plants could not have achieved the success they have in populating the surface of the earth.

8

The Cell in Development

In the past few chapters, casual reference has been made to the fact that organisms "develop" from a fertilized egg to a plant or animal of adult proportions. Each of us knows in a general way what is meant by development: it is a continuous and gradual process that takes time in order to be fully realized, is generally accompanied by an increase in size and weight, involves the appearance of new features and new functions, and eventually slows down when mature dimensions are reached. Man, for example, develops from the fertilized egg stage through prenatal life, childhood, adolescence, sexual maturity, physical maturity, middle age, senility, and death. Development is, of course, one of the most prominent features in the early life of an organism, but the formation of new blood cells, gametes, and wound tissue, which may take place up to death at an advanced age, are also aspects of development. These terms we have used, however, are only broadly descriptive and tell us very little about the mechanism of development as a biological phenomenon. We must approach development from the cellular level, since the cell remains the building block of life. And we must ask how the potentialities of the fertilized egg, which reside as coded information in the egg's DNA and in the organization of its cytoplasm, can become the fully-realized features of a perfectly formed organism, with each organ being the right size, in its allotted place, and equipped with the cells to perform properly.

The problem of development in its entirety is an immense and complicated one, and here we wish only to consider the major aspects of development, i.e., *growth, differentiation,* and *integration,* and the role of the cell in each of them.

Growth

Growth is defined as an increase in mass. This increase can result from an enlargement of cells, but more often it is caused by an increase in the number of cells through mitotic divisions. Growth, then, is essentially a process of replication: the original cell takes from its environment the raw materials it needs and converts them into more substance and more cells like itself. Let us consider the human egg. It weighs about one-millionth of a gram, and the sperm, at fertilization, adds to it only another five-billionths of a gram. At birth, however, a child will weigh around 7 pounds, or 3200 grams, which is an increase of about one billion times during a nine-month period. A newborn child is obviously not simply a mass of cells of comparable size and character to the original cell; if it were, it would just be a ball of cells devoid of human qualities. Nor was its growth rate uniform throughout its prenatal life. Other processes must act to mold these cells into shape, as a potter or a sculptor molds his clay, and to stamp them with character.

One of these processes is the *relative rate of growth.* This rate determines form, which is another way of saying that some parts of the body grow at a faster or slower rate than others, and that some features come into existence early, and others later, in development. Figure 48 shows how the growth rate in the human alters the relative proportions of bodily parts to each other. The head and neck increase in size very rapidly, the arms grow faster at an earlier stage than do the legs, while the body progresses at a more or less steady rate until maturity.

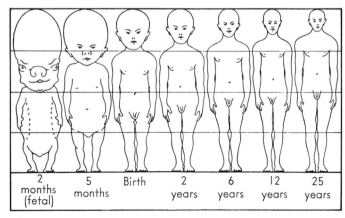

Fig. 48. Changes in the form and proportion of the human body during fetal and postnatal life. (From H. B. Glass, *Genes and the Man*. New York: Teachers College, Columbia Univ., Bureau of Publications, 1943, after Morris.)

| 2 months (fetal) | 5 months | Birth | 2 years | 6 years | 12 years | 25 years |

Growth, therefore, is not just the multiplication of cells; it is a complicated pattern of multiplication, with different centers of growth being active at different times and at different rates of development. These centers are coordinated so as to produce an unfolding of form, and it is form, of course, that distingiushes one human from another, all humans from other animals, and an orchid, for example, from a lily.

Differentiation

It is *differentiation,* however, that stamps each cell with its own uniqueness of structure and function. The generalized cell is transformed by a process of progressive change into a specialized one, and variation is thereby introduced into a functioning organism. In man, for example, growing cells are transformed into the myriad of different cells which make up the human body: cells of the nervous, muscular, digestive, excretory, circulatory, and respiratory systems.

Differentiation is a phenomenon that has no counterpart in the non-living world, and what little information we have has been derived from observations of living systems. It is creative in the sense that life is creative, for out of the general features common to all cells arise structures and functions which are peculiar to specialized cells. This can be seen in Fig. 49, which illustrates the origin and progressive differentiation of a special cell type, in this case, the *melanocytes* that form pigment in the human skin. Differentiation, therefore, is to development what mutation is to biological inheritance, and what imagination is to human endeavor; it provides variety.

Differentiation, of course, has its limitations, and these limits are determined by the genetic information in the nucleus. A beautiful experiment on *Acetabularia* illustrates this (Fig. 20). By grafting experiments, it was demonstrated that the character of the cap was determined by the nucleus, not by the cytoplasm, even though differentiation takes place in the cytoplasm. The nucleus, therefore, controls differentiation by exercising its influence on the self-perpetuating bodies in the cytoplasm: mitochondria, plastids, microsomes, etc.

Differentiation may be both quite profound and very simple in its final effect. Nerve and muscle cells of higher animals, and the cotton fibers or water-conducting cells of higher plants, represent rather profound modifications through differentiation. Other modifications at least appear to be much simpler. Two of these take place in *Pandorina* (Fig. 16), one of which—the transformation of a vegetative cell to a sexual gamete—has already been mentioned. The other modification affects the colony as a whole. When the colony is newly formed as a result of successive mitotic divisions and is released from the mother cell, certain outer cells on opposite sides turn in slightly to give the colony a somewhat elongated shape and a bilateral symmetry. Then the red eyespots at one end diminish in

Fig. 49. The origin and course of differentiation of melanin-producing cells in the human. Top, the melanoblasts have their origin in an area called the neural crest, from which they migrate and differentiate. Their ultimate fate depends on whether they end up in the dermis or epidermis; if in the former, they cease producing melanin except in special circumstances, but if in the epidermis, they continue to produce melanin until death. Below, five cells, showing the series of changes that are undergone from the round melanoblast (left) to the highly differentiated melanocyte (far right). (Courtesy of Dr. A. A. Zimmermann, from A. A. Zimmermann and S. W. Becker, Jr., *Illinois Monographs in Medical Sciences*, VI, 1939, 1–39.)

A

Neural crest, the presumed source of pigment-forming cells, showing the characteristic splitting into two strands of migrating cells.

B

The earliest *migrating melanoblasts* cannot be distinguished from mesenchymal cells (4th-9th wk).

C

Immature melanocytes in the fetal dermis.

D

Migrate to epidermis

Remain in dermis

Melanocytes maturing in the epidermis. These produce melanin throughout life.

In the human dermis, melanoblasts were first identified as round cells beginning to form melanin (10th wk).

Melanocytes maturing in the dermis. These produce melanin only until birth, in localized areas (Mongolian spot) or abnormally in Blue Nevi.

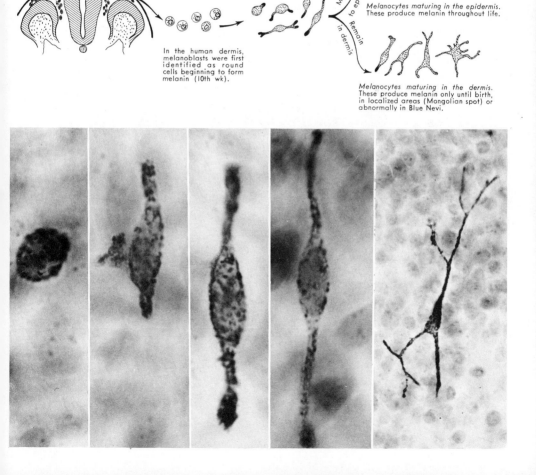

intensity, giving the colony an anterior-posterior axis with a primitive head and tail region that is manifested by swimming movements and certain reactions to light.

Another simple differentiation, one that is dependent on position, takes place in the formation of pollen grains of higher plants. Ordinarily, the axis of microspore division is at a 45° angle to the axis of the second meiotic division (Fig. 50), giving a microspore with a tube and a generative nucleus. The generative nucleus comes to lie against what was the inner wall of the microspore, and it soon doubles its amount of DNA in preparation for its division into two sperm cells. The tube nucleus, however, does not double its amount of DNA. The differentiation undergone by the two nuclei is a matter of position; if the position is changed as a result of an altered axis of division, the two nuclei behave differently, a distinction between tube and generative nuclei cannot be made, and the pollen grain is non-functional. How position determines the reaction of the two nuclei is unknown.

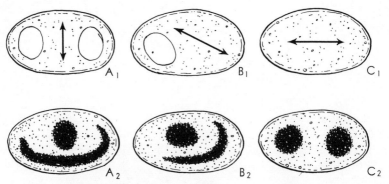

Fig. 50. • Microspores of the spiderwort, *Tradescantia*, showing how the axis of division (arrow in upper row) influences the type of nuclei formed in the mature pollen grain (bottom row). Vacuoles in the cell (top line) determine the original axis of division.

DIFFERENTIATION VS. GROWTH

If we contrast differentiation with growth, we find, without knowing why, that these processes tend to be mutually exclusive. Where growth is, to varying degrees, an unending process of multiplication of similar units, differentiation is the extraction of these units from the mass, thus making them different. In the process, differentiation tends to prevent the further multiplication of the cell and, therefore, the more differentiated a cell has become, the less likely it is to divide. The cell thus commits itself to a course of action it cannot readily change.

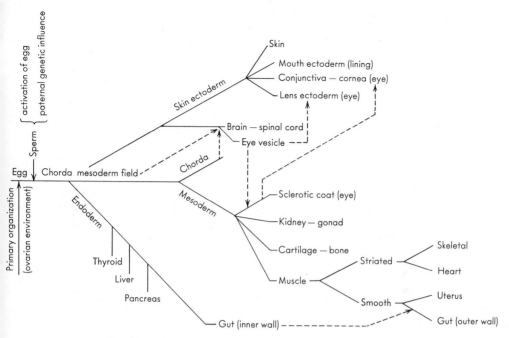

Fig. 51. Diagrammatic representation of the pattern of progressive differentiation from the unfertilized egg to the more mature tissues in a vertebrate. The three major tissue layers (ectoderm, mesoderm, and endoderm) originate early and progressively give rise to the cells of the major organs. Dashed lines indicate an influence of one tissue on another during the course of development. Note that the eye has a double origin from both ectoderm and mesoderm. (Courtesy of Dr. B. H. Willier.)

Let us examine a bit more closely what we mean when we say a cell is "committed." Figure 51 shows diagrammatically the course of development in vertebrate animals. When the cells near their final delineation into mature, differentiated structures, their potentiality for further change

Fig. 52. A scheme to illustrate how an uncommitted cell (represented by a ball) may become committed to a particular fate by rolling down one of the channels of differentiation, from which it cannot return. (After C. H. Waddington, *The Strategy of the Genes.* New York: Macmillan, 1957.)

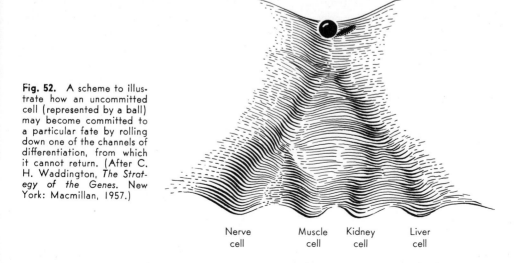

is narrowed as their specialization becomes more pronounced. Professor Waddington, the English embryologist, has very neatly expressed this idea of commitment by his diagram of a developmental landscape (Fig. 52). The generalized cell is visualized as a ball rolling downhill toward its final destiny, and this destiny depends on which of the many valleys the ball rolls through.

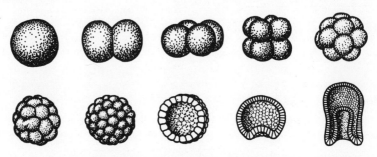

Fig. 53. Early developmental stages of Amphioxus from the egg (top left) through the blastula (bottom middle) to the gastrula (bottom right) stages. Although the size of the embryo remains much the same until gastrulation (infolding), cell size and shape are being constantly altered by division and the pressure of adjoining cells. (Reprinted with permission from R. Gerard, *Unresting Cells.* New York: Harper, 1949.)

Let us express what we have been saying in more specific terms. Figure 53 illustrates the general course of early development in an animal such as Amphioxus. If the four-celled stage is shaken apart, we find that each cell is capable of developing into a normal, if slightly smaller, tadpole; this will occur even if the *blastula* is pinched in two by a hair loop. If we wait until the *gastrula* stage to disrupt the development, however, only abnormal and incompletely formed individuals will result. Something obviously has been lost by the cells of the gastrula that was present in earlier ones, and the two halves of the severed embryo are no longer equivalent. Thus the destiny of some cells has already been determined even though no obvious change has taken place, and each part can only perform its "committed" role.

The embryologist has another way of approaching this problem. He cuts certain cells out of an embryo and transplants them to other embryos. If he transplants a group of young and undifferentiated cells to the future head region of another embryo, the transplanted cells become part of the head region; if he transplants them to the back, they will become part of the back musculature; if to the posterior part, they become part of the tail. However, if he transplants cells from an older embryo in the same way, these cells have been "committed"; instead of becoming an integral part of the region to which they are transplanted, they tend rather to retain their own identity and even to modify the surrounding cells. This is well illustrated by an experiment done in the chick embryo. If the leg bud, having no resemblance to a mature leg in any way, is removed from a young chick embryo and is transplanted to the body cavity of another embryo, the cells in the bud live, continue to increase in number, and eventually form a very well-developed leg with bones and muscles (Fig. 54). Yet the bud at the time of transplantation possessed no bone or muscle cells. In terms of Waddington's landscape, however, they had already entered a "valley" leading to leg formation, a valley down which they continued to roll and from which they could not escape.

DIFFERENTIATION AS LOSS OR ACQUISITION

Differentiation, consequently, begins long before any visible change takes place in the cells. Such changes, of course, must be preceded by chemical alterations which the cell apparently cannot undo once they have occurred. We must admit, however, that our present knowledge of these changes and the cause of their initiation is fragmentary indeed. There seems to be no doubt, on the other hand, that the differentiation of cells

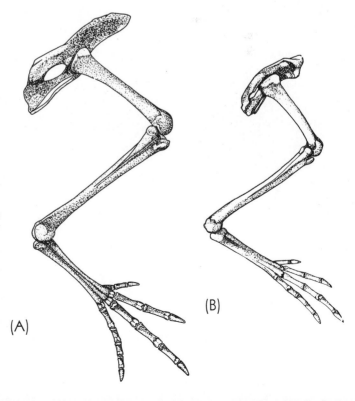

Fig. 54. An example of a structure that develops after transplantation in a reasonably normal fashion. (A) Normal leg bones of a chick 18 days after incubation; (B) A slightly smaller but a reasonably complete set of leg bones which developed after the hind limb bud (similar to the limb buds shown in Fig. 60) was transplanted to the body cavity. At the time of transplantation, the limb bud showed no evidence of bone or muscle, but the cells had already been "committed" to leg formation, a process of differentiation which continued even though the limb bud had been removed to a foreign location. (V. Hamburger and M. Waugh, *Physiological Zoology*, XIII, 1940, 367–380.)

(A)

(B)

can occur either by the *loss of old functions* or by the *acquisition of new ones*. We should now examine this in somewhat greater detail, for loss and acquisition may not be quite so opposite as the words imply.

A mature nerve cell traces its ancestry back to the original fertilized egg, although it is, of course, very different from the egg, both in its morphology and in its function. Irreversible changes occur along the way, and the early versatility of the egg is sacrificed for the special property of conduction which characterizes nerves. Since if a nerve is cut, the axon can be repaired, it has not lost all power of repair, but it cannot, on the other hand, divide to form new nerve cells. If a nerve cell dies, therefore, it cannot be replaced, but this loss in the power of division is compensated for by the acquisition of a new ability, namely, the capacity to conduct electrical impulses rapidly and efficiently.

We could, of course, assume that the original egg was capable of doing all the things that each differentiated cell can do, and that these abilities, residing in various parts of the cell, were segregated out by cell division. This possibility seems unlikely, however, when we consider that each of the cells of an early embryo can, when shaken apart, form normal individuals. More likely is the supposition that the egg contains, in the coded information in its DNA, the potentiality of all properties of all cells,

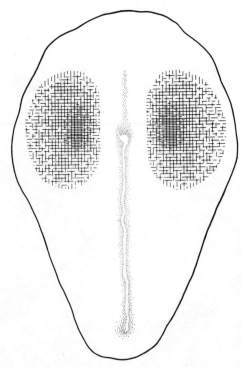

Fig. 55. The heart-forming areas of the chick embryo from which cells can migrate into the site where actual formation takes place. The cells move first toward the tail and then through the region of the primitive streak (stippled area) into the mesoderm (middle layer of cells), after which they assemble in the head area on either side of the primitive streak. The intensity of the cross-hatching is a measure of the number of cells coming from a given area. (Courtesy of Dr. Mary E. Rawles.)

and that as the differentiation of cells takes place, some potentialities are accentuated as others are suppressed or even lost. A consideration of the development of the chicken heart will make this clear.

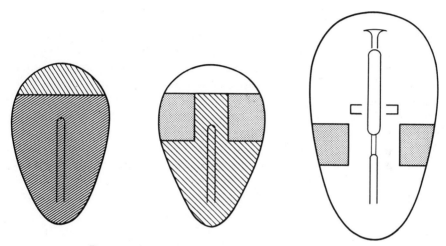

Fig. 56. The distribution of heart-muscle proteins in three stages of the chick embryo. Heart actin (dotted area) is formed later than heart myosin (cross-hatched area) and in a much more restricted area of the embryo, but myosin formation itself becomes more restricted as the embryo develops. The density of cross-hatching indicates the intensity of myosin formation. (Courtesy of Dr. James Ebert.)

The chicken heart begins to appear as a morphologically visible structure about twenty-four hours after incubation, and the first heart beats occur early in the second day. The cells that form the heart migrate from other regions into the heart-forming area, as indicated in Fig. 55, but what we want to know is when the heart-forming cells first become identified as potential heart cells. To find this out we determine at what stage the cells begin to form chemical substances peculiar to heart cells. These substances are proteins, and 75 per cent of the heart protein consists of *actin, myosin,* and *tropomyosin,* the proteins that are necessary for muscle contraction. Heart myosin, however, is different from leg-muscle myosin and can be distinguished from it by chemical tests. Tests for actin and myosin reveal that these proteins are more generally formed by cells of the early embryo than by older embryos (Fig. 56), and the myosin appears earlier and in more widespread fashion than does actin, although both are localized later in the same region. It is possible that the localization occurs through the migration of cells, but it is more likely that some cells lose their ability to synthesize myosin, while others in the heart-forming region have this ability accentuated.

The interesting point is that heart cells can be recognized chemically long before they have either reached the heart region or have assumed a shape characteristic of heart-muscle cells. Also, if we interfere with the early synthesis of myosin by giving the cells an inhibitor, antimycin A, we can prevent the formation of the heart.

These heart studies emphasize the fact that the differentiation of cells is essentially a change in cellular proteins. Most, if not all, the morphological features of the cell have proteins in their chemical make-up; a change in these features is undoubtedly a reflection of a previous alteration in the proteins. A change in metabolic function must also involve a protein change, because all reactions in the cell are governed by enzymes which themselves are proteins. Since the nuclei of most somatic cells appear similar, we must therefore assume that most cellular alterations that occur during differentiation take place in the cytoplasm. As a further corollary, since particular cell strains can increase and perpetuate their kind, the cytoplasm as well as the nucleus must be endowed with the capacity for self-perpetuation. We do not yet know what this means in chemical terms.

NUCLEAR DIFFERENTIATION

The nucleus itself can undergo a degree of differentiation. We can think of the nucleus as having a set of genes containing coded information in its DNA that exercises control over the cell and directs its destiny. But is the nucleus of a liver cell the same as that of a nerve cell? Are all genes active at all times? The answer is probably "no" in both instances, even though the critical information is difficult to obtain. But certain experiments suggest a solution. For example, with very fine pipettes it is possible to take a nucleus from a cell of the blastula and put it into an egg that has had its own nucleus removed. Such an egg will withstand puncturing and develop normally. However, if a nucleus is taken from a later embryo after the gastrula stage and transplanted similarly to an enucleated egg, development is only partial and is abnormal. The nuclei from differentiated, or "committed," cells are restricted in their developmental control, and they lack the versatility of the nuclei of undifferentiated cells. We do not yet know how this restriction of power arises, but it does suggest that the differentiation of cells can be both cytoplasmic and nuclear.

We also know that chromosomes often exhibit a morphological differentiation. In the larvae of flies such as *Drosophila melanogaster*, the cells of the salivary glands contain very large, banded chromosomes, as shown in Fig. 57. They arise by the growth and elongation of ordinary chromosomes, and their appearance in different tissues during development may also change. Whether the changes, which affect the appearance of particular bands in the chromosomes, indicate that the genes in these areas are particularly active at one stage but not at another is a possibility that needs further exploration.

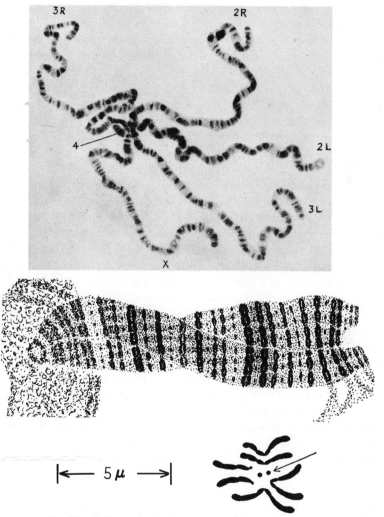

Fig. 57. Salivary-gland chromosomes of *Drosophila melanogaster*. Top, a smear preparation from the salivary gland of a female, showing the X-chromosome, the arms of the two autosomes (2L, 2R, 3L, and 3R), and the small 4-chromosome. The diploid number of chromosomes is present, but the homologues are in intimate synapsis, and are united by their centric heterochromatin into a chromocenter. Middle, enlarged drawing of the 4-chromosome showing the banded structure; the diffuse chromocenter is at the left, and the two homologues are intimately paired. Bottom, metaphase chromosomes from a ganglion cell, with an arrow pointing to the 4-chromosomes, and with a scale to indicate differences in size between the two types of chromosomes. (Top, courtesy of Dr. B. P. Kaufmann; middle and bottom, C. B. Bridges, *Journal of Heredity*, 26, 1935, 60–64.)

Integration

We can now appreciate the fact that the fertilized egg is a rather remarkable cell. It is primarily an organism in its simplest or undeveloped state; it is a cell only secondarily, and differs from other cells in its potentiality for total development. Growth and differentiation, as we have seen, are two of the processes by which development is achieved. When we consider development in terms of cells, therefore, we find a progression from initially simple and uniform cell types to complex and diverse ones; the plastic, versatile cell becomes stabilized with an unalterable structure; cells with general functions develop highly specialized functions.

But growth, relative growth rates, and differentiation are not enough to account for all of development. The whole course of development of an organism, from the moment of fertilization to death, is characterized by a *unity* and a *harmony* of structure and behavior that cannot be explained by these processes. The egg, the seed, the embryo, and the larva are all as complete organisms as is the mature individual that arises from them. Although their development may not be fully realized, at all times they behave like, and indeed are, fully functional living entities, and they develop as a *whole,* not simply as a collection of cells or a group of cells.

This phenomenon of unity we call *integration,* but we must admit that it is difficult to define and even more difficult to comprehend. To understand integration we must have an intimate knowledge of organization at the molecular, cellular, tissue, and organ levels, and this we do not possess except in a fragmentary way. We do know that integration depends on a number of factors: chemical stimuli such as hormones; cell movements such as those involved in the formation of the gonads and in the infolding that produces the gastrula; cell interactions such as those responsible for the formation of a compound structure such as the eye (Fig. 51); and the processes of differentiation which impress upon an undeveloped limb bud the ability to form a complete leg even after the bud is removed from its normal position of development (Fig. 54).

We can highlight the significance of integration by posing several questions that we cannot yet answer. Why do animals reach a mature size and stop growing? What determines the life span of organisms? What determines the size relation between one part of the body and another? What is it that determines *morphogenesis,* the origin and realization of form? How does one phase of development affect succeeding phases? We must answer these and many other questions before we begin to understand development as an over-all process of life. Some of the aspects of development can possibly be approached and explained at the cellular level, but others, such as morphogenesis, seem to involve a higher order of organization in which the individual cell plays a subordinate role. And our ability to control cancer, which represents the growth and escape of cells from regulative control, rests on our comprehending development as a rigidly-governed system of chemical checks and balances.

Any individual has a life span that is character-istic of the species to which it belongs. In some instances, the life span is rather sharply limited: 21 days for the rotifers, 17 years for certain periodic locusts. Usu-ally, however, we think of the life span as an average figure: a few days for cer-tain insects, a few months for annual plants, three score and 10 years for man, 250 to 300 years for an oak tree. The sequoia of our West Coast and the bristle-cone pine of California's White Mountains are probably the longest-lived organisms; some of the trees reach an age of several thousand years.

Cells, too, have a life span which they complete and then pass out of ex-istence. And like organisms, cell strains, even in the same organism, have charac-teristic long or short life spans. Yet it is entirely reasonable to consider some cells to be immortal. When a unicellular or-ganism divides, the life of the single cell becomes part of the life of two new cells, and as long as the species lives so does the cell whose life, then, stretches in an unbroken chain back to some original cell in the past. Among sexually repro-ducing organisms, only the cells of the germ line can lay claim to immortality for they are the only cells that span the gen-erations and keep the species alive. But among the cells of the body, death is a very necessary process because if its role is altered the functioning of the organism will be affected drastically. As a biologi-cal problem, there are two broad cate-gories of cellular death: (1) that resulting from the wear and tear of existence, which must be counterbalanced by an equivalent amount of cell replacement, and (2) that resulting from the normal process of development.

Cell Replacement

It has been estimated that a human being has a new body every seven years, the time it takes for the old cells of the body to be replaced by new ones. Even if accurate, this figure is very misleading, for some parts of the body require a constant replacement of cells while other parts are incapable of replacement. By the time of birth, all the nerve and muscle cells of the body have been formed, and they will continue to function as long as the individual lives (barring injury). If a nerve cell is destroyed, it is not replaced by another; the nerve cell cannot divide once it is fully differentiated, and no nerve-cell replacement center exists. It was thought that this was also true for muscle cells, but recent studies suggest that the muscles are capable of limited replacement. The fact that an organ remains constant in size, however, is not indicative of its rate of replacement; unless the cellular conditions are known, the constancy of size merely indicates that there is no net gain or loss of cells. The death of the old cells is equalled by the production of new cells.

Some biologists estimate that the human body loses 1 to 2 per cent of its cells through death each day. Body weight, therefore, would double every 50 to 100 days if no cell death occurred. If the weight of the body remains constant, therefore, these cells must be replaced by new ones, by billions of cells every day. Since none of these is produced in the muscles or the nervous tissue, there must be and are some very active centers of death and replacement in, for instance, the protective layers, and in the blood, digestive, and reproductive systems. The other organs of the body have much slower replacement rates; the liver cell, for example, has an average life span of about 18 months. Consequently, if we look at a liver slice under the microscope, we expect to find very few cells in division. On the other hand, if a portion of the human liver is lost, the rate of cell replacement is stepped up until the original size is once more approximated.

The outer surface of the human body is covered with a protective layer, most of which is skin, but which also includes the lining of all openings, the cornea of the eye, and such modified skin derivatives as nails and hair. The cells of these structures are constantly being lost through death: the skin sloughs off, and the growing nails and hair are composed of dead cells. The process of replacement, then, must be a relatively rapid one. The underlying cells are constantly dividing, and are pushed outward toward the skin surface, while the outermost cells become *cornified* (hardened) as they die (Fig. 58). It takes approximately 12 to 14 days for a cell in the skin of the forearm to move from the dividing to the outermost layer of the skin. Callouses on the hands are thickened areas of dead cells, and a needle can be pushed through these areas without pain or drawing blood.

The cornea of the eye is a special type of skin in which the rate of cell death and replacement is high. The cornea, in fact, is an excellent type of tissue to examine for active cell division. Since it is only a few cell-layers thick, it can be stripped off (the salamander and rat are good animals to use for this purpose), fixed, stained, and mounted intact on a microscope slide. The dying cells can be seen at the outer surface, while the underneath cells are in active division.

The cells of the blood are not formed in the blood. The red blood cells are derived from the bone marrow, and the white cells (*leucocytes*)

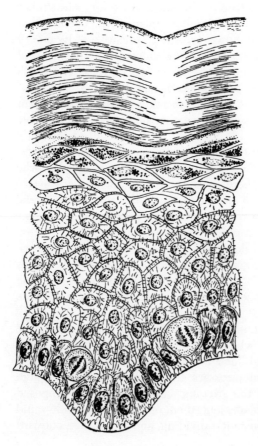

Fig. 58. Section through human skin showing the progression of cells from the region of division at the base up to the horny layer of dead cells at the surface. The surface layer is continuously eroded away, but is being as continuously replaced by cells moving into place from below.

from the lymph nodes, spleen, and thymus gland. Together, these cells and the *plasma* constitute the blood, which has an average ratio of one white cell to 400–500 red cells. The blood-forming areas usually manage to maintain the cell ratios, but obviously there must be a high loss of cells to offset the new ones formed or the blood system would clog up. Since each type of cell dies off at a relatively constant rate, we need consider here only one, the red blood cells. Their life span is about 120 days. They do not possess a nucleus, which is lost as they pass into the blood stream, so the wear of passage through the vessels cannot be repaired, and they grow fragile and finally burst. Certain types of illness may shorten their life span. In a patient with pernicious anemia, the life span is reduced to about 85 days; with sickle-cell anemia, to 42 days. The rate of replacement cannot keep up with the loss of cells, and the red-cell count falls below normal and results in an anemic state. The cause of the shortened life span is not known. The digestive system is another organ with a cell death rate that is very high. Figures for the human are not known, but it has been estimated that the cells lining the intestine of the rat are replaced every 38 hours.

In the plant kingdom, we find that the lower plants—the algae and fungi, in particular—have a rather low loss of cells through death. In the higher plants, however, the rate is enormous. In herbaceous plants, all the cells above ground are lost every season. But consider a large tree. The annual loss of cells in the leaves, flowers, and fruits (only the seeds remain alive) is high enough, but when all the cells going to form dead wood and bark are added, the loss of cells through death in animals is small by comparison. Yet a high rate of cell death is as much a pattern of existence as the continuation of living cells.

Cell Death and Normal Development

When we think of normal development, we naturally think of an increase in the number of cells, their subsequent differentiation into specialized cells, and the grouping of these cells into organs and organ systems. This process is a dynamic and creative one, and you may consider it incongruous to characterize cell death as a vital and necessary aspect of development. Cell death, however, plays two very significant roles in development. The first of these, *metamorphosis*, has long been known; the second, the role of cell death in the shaping of organs and body contours, is only beginning to be appreciated as a phase of development.

Metamorphosis involves a change in shape (the transformation of a larval form of an organism into an adult shape) and a change in organs when one mode of life is exchanged for another. Two well-known examples are the metamorphosis of a tadpole into an adult frog, and of a caterpillar into a pupa and then into a butterfly or a moth.

A tadpole is transformed into a frog without an appreciable change in size, and in the common American leopard frog the process takes about a year. The tadpole that emerges from the egg, and the large tadpole about to metamorphose have the same general shape; in its conversion into a frog, it grows legs and loses its tail, which is devoured by wandering cells, or *phagocytes,* that are carried by the blood stream to the tail region where they gradually consume the muscles, nerves, skin, and other tissues. The skin shrinks and eventually the tail is reduced to a mere stump. In addition, the tissues in the digestive and excretory systems are extensively reorganized. We can speed up or slow it down experimentally, for in the frog metamorphosis is, at least in part, under the control of an iodine-containing hormone from the *thyroid gland.* More thyroid hormone accelerates the process, less reduces its speed and may even prolong larval life and shape indefinitely.

The character of metamorphosis in insects varies quite widely, and cell death is not always a major aspect of change. In the simplest type of metamorphosis, the cells of a particular larval tissue are retained to form the corresponding tissue in the adult, and only minor differences in growth and differentiation are needed to bring this about. In these cases of *incomplete metamorphosis,* the form of the insect is only slightly altered as the larva matures to adult proportions. Good examples of this type of metamorphosis are found in the locust, grasshopper, or cockroach.

In *complete metamorphosis,* the larval and adult forms are totally different from each other. The larva, or caterpillar, is converted into a pupa, the larval skin hardens and shrinks into the outer skin, or *puparium,* of the pupa, and the larval tissues are almost completely destroyed. The adult develops during pupation, and adult tissues arise from *imaginal buds* that form in the larva and that escape cell death. These buds can be regarded as zones of persistent embryonic tissue in which the potentiality for growth and differentiation is suppressed during larval life, and is only realized when the *juvenile hormone* controlling larval growth lessens its activity and the hormone concerned with metamorphosis takes over.

Figure 59 shows the location of certain imaginal buds of the larva of the fruit fly, *Drosophila.* Much of the brain and nervous system will survive cell destruction, but the intestine, blood system, muscles, and skin will be totally destroyed.

The last type of cell death we will consider is that involved in the shaping of organs. Form, therefore, can be achieved by relative rates of cell death as well as by relative rates of cell growth. As organs develop during morphogenesis, for instance, excess cells are often a hindrance, and these transient cells that are of use to the embryo or larva but not to the adult must be removed (the tail of the tadpole is a case in point). Or when an organism forms secretory ducts, cells die instead of pulling apart to provide for the central hole or lumen. Many organs form by the infolding of tissues which then fuse along their edges—for example, the eye and part of the nervous system—and the seams where fusion takes place are removed by cell death. Fingers and toes are separated from each other in the same way; if the separation is incomplete, a webbed condition results.

One of the most arresting instances of cell death as a morphogenetic phenomenon is the one that frees the elbow of the wing of the chick from the body wall and gives the wing its characteristic shape. Figure 60 illustrates the region in question. These cells die as a line of cellular destruc-

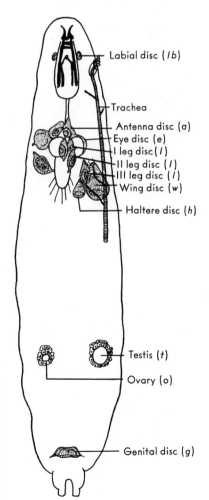

Labial disc (*l b*)

Trachea

Antenna disc (*a*)
Eye disc (*e*)
I leg disc (*l*)
II leg disc (*l*)
III leg disc (*l*)
Wing disc (*w*)

Haltere disc (*h*)

Testis (*t*)

Ovary (*o*)

Genital disc (*g*)

Fig. 59. Imaginal buds in a mature larva of *Drosophila*. During metamorphosis most of the larval structures except the nervous system will undergo destruction, while the adult tissues will arise from the imaginal buds, some of which are indicated. The buds form during larval life, but do not undergo extensive growth and differentiation into adult structures until the influence of the larval hormones wanes. (Reprinted with permission by Dietrich Bodenstein from *Biology of Drosophila*, M. Demerec, New York: Wiley, 1950.)

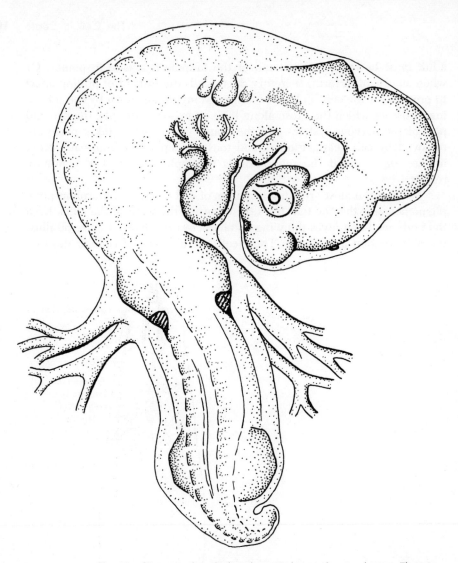

Fig. 60. Diagram of a chick embryo 72 hours after incubation. The wing buds are beginning to form below the head region, and it is the cells in the cross-hatched areas that will die in order to cut out the "elbow" region.

tion moves from the body area along the front and back of the wing toward its tip, thus separating the elbow region from the body wall. Most fascinating of all, however, is the fact that when these cells are removed and transplanted to another part of the embryo, the cells *die on schedule* (at approximately 4 days of age) as if they were still in their original site. Their time of death had already been determined by some unknown change that had taken place within them, and once embarked on their course of destruction they could not escape. If we can, in the future, understand the mechanism responsible for this phenomenon, we may well be on our way to comprehending the larger problem of aging and of fixed life spans.

Selected Readings

Butler, J. A. V., *Inside the Living Cell.* New York: Basic Books, 1959. A nontechnical account of cell structure and function and of the reactions of cells to radiations, chemicals, cancer, and aging.

Darlington, C. D., *Chromosome Botany.* London: Allen & Unwin, 1956. An account of nuclear cytology as it relates to the evolution of plant species.

Gerard, R. W., *Unresting Cells.* New York: Harper, 1940. One of the finest books available on cells; should be read by every student of biology.

Greeson, R. A. R., *Essentials of General Cytology.* Edinburgh: University Press, 1948. A sound general account of both nuclear and cytoplasmic cytology.

Hoffman, J. G., *The Life and Death of Cells.* New York: Hanover, 1957. A semipopular account of the microscopic realm of cells, as viewed through modern theories of matter and energy.

Hughes, A., *A History of Cytology.* New York: Abelard-Schuman, 1959. An excellent historical account of microscopical observations, the cell theory, cell division, theories of inheritance, studies of the cytoplasm, and the place of cellular theory in general biology.

McLeish, J., and B. Snoad, *Looking at Chromosomes.* New York: St. Martin's Press, 1958. A small book describing mitotic and meiotic divisions in the lily, and illustrated by a superb collection of photographs.

Maximow, A. A., and W. Bloom, *A Textbook of Histology.* Philadelphia: Saunders, 1957. Widely used by medical students, this is one of the best American texts available in its field; beautifully illustrated in color and in black and white.

Swanson, C. P., *Cytology and Cytogenetics.* Englewood Cliffs, N.J.: Prentice-Hall, 1957. A detailed account of chromosomal structure and behavior, particularly as these relate to genetics and evolution.

Wilson, E. B., *The Cell in Development and Heredity.* New York: Macmillan, ·1925. A classic of biological literature, with discussions oriented toward embryology; worth while for both beginner and expert.

Index

Index

109